Mike Sargent was born i 1941. He was educated a the Street, 'Galdeford Uni Technical College. Most c spent in London in a var driver, bricklayer, club and theatre manager and ice cream salesman. He has worked in France as a builder and driven trucks from London to Greece. He now lives in Ludlow with his wife and son Jack.

# MY OLD MAN THE GASMAN

by

Mike Sargent

EXCELLENT PRESS
LUDLOW

Excellent Press
Palmers House
7 Corve Street
Ludlow
Shropshire SY8 1 DB


First published by Excellent Press 1998

ISBN 1 900318 09

Printed and bound in Great Britain

# *Acknowledgements*

With thanks to

Howard Cheese and Kate Andrew from Ludlow Museum.

Helen Ford from the National Gas Archives BG plc, Partington, Manchester.

Alan Baker
Frank Acton
Kevin Bamford
and my wife
Roselyne Sargent

and all the other citizens of our town for their help and encouragement.

# 1    *Over the Hill*

In the middle of this summer the central heating
went wrong. The hot water was all right, it was just
that the heating stopped working and since we
didn't want any heating I left it for the annual
check. But there was no news from the gas board,
no letter informing me of the annual check.

Thirty years ago I would have walked round to
the gas showrooms and told them about it, they
would have recognised me without asking who I
was and then they would have sent my Dad or Bob
Jacks or Ernie Ward round and it would have been
fixed. Or perhaps I would have seen one of them in
the street and told them that my gas needed looking at and then they would have said:

'Is it important?'

and I would have said:

'No, it just needs doing before the winter.'

If I'd have told them there was a smell of gas
then they would have most probably come straight
round on their own bat, made out a job ticket
themselves and that would have been that. Now you
have to phone Glasgow on an 0800 number and a
woman with a Scottish accent asks you to give your
post code and as she bangs that code into a ter-
minal she asks you 'What number?' and you think
that it's your telephone number that she wants, so

when you have given it to her she says, 'Your house number. THE NUMBER OF YOUR HOUSE IN THE STREET.'

And so you apologise to her because you cannot understand why she wants your house number since she has not yet asked for the name of your street. But she does not need it, it is in the post code … and we thought that when the post codes first came out thirty years ago that they were of no importance, but they are, yes they are …

And when you have given the woman the number of your house she will say, 'Mr Sargent' and you just cannot understand how in God's name she knows your name so you are thrown, and almost forget to tell her that you would like someone to come round and look at the gas central heating system and she tells you that you have only one more month left on your five star maintenance system and that if payment is not received you will not have a five star maintenance system and so to be on the safe side would you please make payment … Sir!

You mentally make a note of the fact that she called you a Sir. And then you tell her that the central heating system is not working, but that the hot water system *is* working …

'Tomorrow morning … Sir!'

And you are not quite sure what she means. You just cannot understand how a woman in Glasgow could possibly send a fitter out at such short notice and then you realise that if she is able to give you your name with just the post code and the street number and the exact date you paid your last bill, then she must know the whereabouts of every gas fitter in the country, so I have to explain to her that I work nights and like to sleep during the mornings. Now that she knows that I work nights she'll probably enter that into the details that she has on me … which is more frightening and makes me kind of paranoid and so we agree to a date next week when I'm not working nights and I thank her and put the phone down and make a cup of coffee.

When he did come the gas fitter was equipped with a lap top computer and dark glasses. He told me that if the system needed a spare part then he would fax it and it would come from Milton Keynes next day. I had visions of Omega delivering a widget halfway across the country and then I realised why there are so many next day services and why our roads are so crowded and I remembered the store-room at the gas works when my Dad worked there and how it was full of every nut, bolt, of every fitting that you could need to sustain a service in our town, of how everything that they ever wanted came by railway because it was all planned in advance and that the investment in the actual physical stock was massive. But probably not so great as the investment in software today which must be some huge amount, her in Glasgow knowing my name and the whereabouts of every gas fitter in the country and on top of that being able to locate every part of every central heating system on the face of the earth and order it for next day by means of a modem on a lap top …

What it's all about is control, control of the work-force and control of the customer. That's what makes it so efficient.

The stories in this book are about a time when people like my Dad worked the length and breadth of this land without a lap top or dark glasses, when all the servicing and maintenance of every appliance in our town was done on a carrier bike. When they made the gas in the town. When you were a part of the community. When in general people cared for each other. When there was a niceness in the air. It was a time when you could buy a glass of cider for two pence halfpenny because there was no tax on cider. It was a time when there were tobacconists in small towns, when you could buy a green cigar, when scissors sharpeners used to come round with grinding wheels on a contraption like a bicycle. When the ragman used to ring the bell from a horse and cart and when everything that was worth anything was recycled.

It was a time when if someone died then every curtain in the street used to be drawn as a sign of respect. It was a time when if your mother was ill then the next door neighbour used to leave hot meals on the table.

It is no good saying that they were better times because they were not, they were harder times. But there was some kind of self respect that we seem to have lost. No one calls you Mister any more, you can't go into a shop and have an assistant say to you:

'Ah, good morning, Mr Sargent.'

It's just 'Sir'.

Even in the small town in which I live it's just 'Sir' now and I can get 'Sir' in Merry Hills shopping centre. And that's the biggest shopping centre in the Midlands!

I can remember laying bricks in an office development in Telford and because I was able to build corners and all the young trowels who had been trained in technical colleges used profiles and so could not build a dog's leg corner and were faster than me and laughed when I had to do my own mixing because I came from a time when there were labourers who did the mixing and carrying and I moaning about how the firm was cutting costs and what kind of shitty job it was that could not afford labourers, shame on me for being there, and they were working through the dinner break, the young ones with cheese sandwiches from a supermarket because their wives could not even make a bait box! Tradesmen eating rubbish sandwiches on the hoof and didn't the agent love it, him with his dark glasses and hard hat and plastic label so that he knew who he was, perhaps it was in case he got lost and never knew how to get back to where he came from on his own without the clerk of the works. They always seemed to be together.

And that is just the working part of your life. The other circle of events that kept families fed, the back garden, has completely disappeared.

If you spend a few hours walking around our town or your town, you will see how people who inherited homes with large gardens have sold their gardens, you will see where once kitchen vegetables grew, now houses sit, planned without any gardens, just hanging baskets or window boxes. Instead you'll see cars and garages and small backyards sometimes paved so that plastic chairs and tables can be sat upon because the owners have so much time to spare and bar-b-q meat that has been marinated in fine sauces that originated in far away countries. We have a much higher standard of living now, we have no need to be self-sufficient in vegetables. We have also lost all our primary tastes.

Once we ate new potatoes that had been dug an hour before, steam cooked and then soaked in butter, and then there were broad beans freshly podded and steamed and home made parsley sauce and the best meat that went with those two vegetables was boiled ham. Full stop. There was nothing else, those four tastes on our plate and we did not bolt our food down, we waited for the slowest, my sister, to finish, and then my father would roll a cigarette and the dog would rest her head on his leg, and that would be the end of the evening meal. If it was midday then we had pudding, we never had pudding after an evening meal and we never had cider or wine or any other alcohol with any meal. My mother was a Baptist. Alcohol was never allowed in our house.

After such a meal my father would move out of the house up to his shed and then he would drink a glass of cider. If it was during the first quarter he would draw the cider from the six gallon barrel; if it was after the start of summer time then the cider would be in the gas refrigerator in quart bottles. It would be cooled and sometimes if it had started to turn it would be slightly effervescent.

If it was during the first quarter then we would not have been eating new potatoes or broad beans, we would have had instead baked potatoes and perhaps diced swede, or maybe swede and turnip, mashed, with some kind of greens, or perhaps salted runner beans, but whatever we ate it was always from the garden. Beef and lamb we bought; rabbit, chicken, pork, all came home cured from the garden or 'The Estate' as my father called our small patch. A small patch, mind you, not just a back yard.

Good Friday was the first day of the gardening. Of course Dad had been at it during the winter, but Good Friday was the day it really started in earnest. You could walk down our street Good Friday morning and all you would hear would be spades cutting into the soil. Some, the winter diggers, would be just forking over the soil but mostly it was digging and they would only straighten up if a train went by and then the diggers waved at the driver who would pull on his whistle.

It would normally start to rain Good Friday afternoon, 'Jesus weeping', mother would say. And then we would stand inside the shed door and look in a westerly direction just in case it started to brighten up. Saturdays were usually better days so by Saturday evening the whole of the top patch had been dug.

If you went to the Hen and Chickens public house either Good Friday or Easter Saturday then you would see a dozen shining spades leaning up against the back wall and perhaps you would see Fred Jordan's push bike leaning there amongst the spades.

The Hen and Chicks was a singing pub. If you could sing then you would be allowed your turn and when your turn came Sid Edwards would shout: 'ORDER, ORDER, LET'S HAVE SOME ORDER'.

And then the pub went quiet and the singer sang his heart out.

No beer was ordered during the singing. Once a fool who should have known better demanded a pint whilst Fred Jordan was singing, 'To be a Farmer's boy'. Sid, the landlord who was behind the bar grabbed him by the throat and hit him so hard that he slumped down in front of the bar where he remained until Fred had finished. Then he was dragged and thrown out into the gutter by Sid who was all the time murmuring under his breath that when he said order he meant order.

That was Easter, then came the early crops, and there was always a race to see who it was had the first peas or early potatoes. One of the gardeners from the big house would always be able to produce fresh peas before the first steeplechase and that was a week before Easter, but that did not really count because he was a professional gardener and knew more about it than any one else. Dad one year grew four roots of potatoes in buckets that he'd pushed into the midden so that we had four roots that flowered the second week in April. He pulled them out and with still soil attached to the tubers, he visited the Wheatsheaf and the Chickens with them in a basket under his arm.

'What ave yer got there, Jack?'

'Oh, just a few new potatoes.'

'There're early, in they?'

'Well, it's quite sheltered under the top patch.'

'Where yer takin them?'

'Just round to the wife's mother. Er's not be so well as er should be.'

'Let's have a look.'

And then whoever it was that asked would feel them, perhaps scraping a little of the skin away just to make sure that they were real.

'You done well there, Jack, what did yer put under um?'

'Oh, I always puts a good layer of rabbit and chicken muck mixed, the chicken muck is too strong on its own, better mixed, and then I puts a little sprinkling of lime to keep the wire worms at bay.'

'Well, Jack, you ave done well,' and then someone else would come in who also had a garden and it would be 'Look what Jack Sargent's got, Jim, a first crop of earlies. What are they, Jack?'

'Aran Pilot.'

'By gum, they are early.'

And then Jim would sink into his seat where he always sat every evening and shake his head and Dad would say:

'I gotta go now, the old mother-in-law likes a few boiled potatoes with her smoked haddock.'

And then the same thing would happen in the Jockey and the Chickens. They would all be at it one way or the other.

Fred Timmis grew great big onions on his allotment in Mill Street. Dad could not grow onions but one year we went to Hanley, up by Stoke-on-Trent, to visit Aunt Cary. Her brother was a champion leek grower and he showed us how he grew leeks which was an extremely complicated affair involving huge holes drilled with a crowbar and packed with manure and requiring earthing up and anchoring with slates and special fine sieved soil. All this explaining had to be done whilst drinking vast quantities of beer and I was so bored eating crisps and Vimto outside the pub ... anyway in spite of the fact that Dad slept all the way back on the train and I had to kick him to wake him when we got to our station, in spite of that, Dad did everything that Aunt Cary's brother told him to do and his leeks grew so big and long that someone in the Horse and Jockey put a sign on his carrier bike that said 'Danger Wide Load'.

After that there were many who came to visit Dad in his shed, to marvel at how the leeks were grown whilst drinking cider, but it never caught on. The only real agriculture show was at Clun, which was not for Ludlow gardeners.

The only competition that sort of caught on in our town was Marrow Rum. You grew a normal sized marrow and then cut the top off it and you removed the centre pips and pith. Next you filled it with brown sugar and put the top of the marrow back on and then you waited for the marrow to get soft. What my Dad used to do was to push in a small tube and then drain out the brown liquid which was like rum and almost as strong. The great thing about it was that mother did not realise that there was any alcoholic kick to it.

Runner beans was another showcase vegetable. It was the length. Mac Knight the barber usually grew the longest and used to carry what you might call samples around in a basket covered in an old tea towel. He used to cut hair in the Charlton Arms Wednesday evenings. During the month of September he would never be without his runner beans. It was only a rumour but there was a suspicion that he used to cut the ends off two beans and then join them. No one had ever seen his beans without the tea towel and since he had once been six feet two inches tall but had shrunk on account of shock he'd suffered in the war it was felt that anything could happen to his beans.

And then they used to kill the pigs and because my Dad was on the council and worked at the gas works and used to do things for people, sometimes he used to bring home the most delicious part of the pig which is that part near to the rear, the tender loin, which consists of two muscles that run along the underside of the backbone. My mother, before she became a complete vegetarian, used to roll it round a stuffing of sage and onion and because she came from the Forest of Dean she used chestnuts as well and we used to blow ourselves out until our bellies touched the table because we knew how to eat.

yes we knew how to eat roast tame rabbit
we knew how to eat new-picked runner beans
we never ever bought onions or shallots
we never ever bought an apple
or a damson or a plum

all I can remember about my early life was that
  it had
a grace and vitality that does not exist any more ...
but perhaps that is because
I'm over the hill

# 2  *Culmington*

After my father was buried my mother sold and moved out of the house I was born in. The house with my Dad's shed and his cider cooling in the great gas refrigerator, the tobacco plants, the pig sty, the rows of shallots, the new potatoes, the chicken runs, the haystack, the bees, the golden rod, the Michaelmas daisies, his fishing rods and all his tools, she sold the lot and moved into a small bungalow with her dog so that she could start again.

She had three lives, before him, with him and after him. I never found out which one she liked best, it was just that after his death the very whiff of masculinity set off in her alarm bells so that the smell of tobacco smoke or a male joke or anything remotely suggesting that a male was necessary would produce a hundred reasons why women could live quite happily without men and that with the aid of a giant sperm bank the second half of our race could be exterminated. There was something heroic about her third life with her dog and her feminist vegetarian beliefs, and yet she was not sure, she was continually justifying them so that it was more than a tragedy when she died a few years before Mrs Jones who was not a vegetarian and liked red roast beef.

My history, that's the history of my family before my time, started in the middle of July on a Saturday afternoon. Dad and I, me sitting on the front carrier of his bike, we were in motion towards Culmington, a village six miles away. There was some kind of dispute about a will. It seemed that our name was not spelt the same as the name of our grandfather and so Dad wanted to check the graves in the village where the family was buried.

It was a solid bright afternoon and by the time we arrived at the churchyard there was a taste of hay in the air. This was because a man who had a finely wrinkled face that held a stumpy pipe and a back bent from work was scything the graveyard with an Isaac. He stopped when we asked him where the Sargents' graves were. And then when Dad said, pointing to the names on the graves, that the spelling was different he said:

'They was changed by the uld school boss in the village school because the surname was pronounced uth the 'A' instead of the 'E'. Had it of bin the 'E' then it uld ave bin Sergant since it was pronounced Sargent uth the 'A' then that was how it should be spelt, so the uld school boss said and he was the boss. The school boss was the boss then, in them days they was the boss, like ... They was from Frawnce, you know, originally, Uld Tom allus said they was. Yes, there was Uld Tom, Young Tom, and Young Tom's son'.

And his eyes glittered with the knowledge that he gave us. While he spoke he continued to sharpen the scythe, his hands moving close to the blade, then he placed the stone into a leather holder on his belt . He never wasted one moment of his time whilst he talked to us, sharpening his lethal blade. The whole action was perfection and in one move-

ment he started to mow again and so we fo
him, straddling the graves, all the time him pu
blue smoke and the scythe swinging and the long
grass falling. The day was warm and close and there
was the smell of freshly cut grass hanging above the
dead. So that what he was doing was something
beautiful and because he really knew how, it was
effortless and a joy to behold.

When he stopped to sharpen he said, 'Uld Tom
was a carpenter and bailiff and six fut two but I
never knewed im, he was jead afore my time, but I
knewed Young Tom. It was Young Tom what killed
the mad bull and it was yer Dad who held the
lamp'.

And then the man stopped sharpening and
pointed to my Dad with his stone.

'That would have bin your father, Young Tom's
son,' he said, 'because it was night when they did it,
Young Tom being out workin', fixin' a roof up the
Bache and so it was dark and Young Tom told yer
Dad not to move an inch and when the bull came at
em he hit it right between the eyes with a pick axe,
what he used fer slaughterin' ... and the bull went
down on his front legs ... jead.'

And the man swung the Isaac. There was a garden fire smouldering behind a stone wall and the
smell of that and the new cut grass mingled and we
followed the man's swinging Isaac until he stopped
again to sharpen the blade and then he told us
about how the mother of Young Tom's son used to
go into Ludlow Market with two baskets under each
arm and how she used to say that she would bring
back a horse with a long tail one day. And he told us
how Uld Tom had a great orchard of apples and
used to make cider and how they used to drink a
couple of gallons a day just as a starter, like.

'By gum, it was good tack,' he said, 'and he used to make perry as well, but the perry worked yer, so you never had it unless you wanted a clear out, like.' He used the word 'like' as a sort of punctuation mark.

'Young Tom's son, your Dad, was a bugger,' he said, 'he used to shoot all the cats, he was pig headed and he left home and went on the lodge. He was a bricklayer and was on the toby fer years until he married yer mother who was in service to a gentleman in Church Stretton.'

We followed the man all over the cemetery until we were back at the entrance to the church and then he told us why there was a carving of a cock on the tomb nearest the church:

'It was because the uld squire used to shoot at the weathercock, peppered it uth lead, he did, and then when he died and they buried the uld bugger that night there was a fearful storm and the cock was blown from off the roof and landed right in the centre of the uld squire's grave and so they carved a cock in the corner of the stone tomb and that's why it's there.'

When the old man had finished telling the tale he cleaned out his pipe and cut the fillings from a piece of twist and once he was fired up he said that he'd got five rows of shallots to hoe and so he turned away from us and Dad and I went towards the bike because there was nothing else to do.

'That explains it,' Dad said.

I had no idea what he was talking about but he was holding me and I could smell his smell that was the smell of earth.

'The apples,' he said, 'that is why we have the oldest apple in England in our garden, the Genet Moyle. That apple came from Rouen, France. Yer

Granddad was always sayin' as how Uld Tom knew more about horticulture an' apples than anyone else and how they used to put orange blossoms over the pips when they planted them so that they would take the taste of the flowers, but Uld Tom said that it was a waste of time and that the finest cider apple came from the Genet Moyle, the only apple that grows from a cuttin', the oldest cider apple in the world, the basic apple of all the cider orchards in Rouen, France.'

It was funny, but from that day on Dad always talked about Rouen as if he knew the town. Anyway, it was the start of something big and my Dad went at it hammer and tongs, writing letters to Somerset House and looking up all the registers of births and deaths and we went for miles all over the country looking at old books in churches, until we found out about the sailing ship that was captured off the south of France by the British 200 years ago with our great great grandfather aboard, horticulturist to Lucien Bonaparte, part of his retinue that was en route to the United States, captured by the British navy with three million pounds sterling on board.

'That explains it,' my father said when he'd finally got the family tree assembled.

'It's all a waste of time,' was my mother's reaction and response.

She felt left out. I never knew why then, but I can understand now. Her side of the tree was ignored, she, a woman living in a patriarchal society, her role was nothing since the line of the children are traced through the male and my mother being a rebellious woman who was a pacifist, who used to read chapters of *Cry Havoc* by Beverley Nichols, one of the first great anti war books, out loud to us, my sister and I, and get carried away when she read it so that it was a cleansing to the bone and all her sayings, like Jesus was the first Socialist, compromise is not permitted, and when the vicar used to come round how she used to ask him why the church had investments in arms and he could not understand because all he wanted was for her to join the mothers' union.

There was no chance of that especially since she used to lie with us under the apple trees naked, worshipping the sun and then when she told Mrs Poole that she was nearer to being a Buddhist than a Christian and that if the Germans were so bad then why did we have a German king? It was a hell of a beginning, for me trying to sort out what was the correct way, but I felt that there was something special about us when Dad said,

'That explains it, we're French stock.'

The way he said it, the word 'stock', sort of very basic, like as if we were from farm animals, and then everything that had ever gone wrong in our family's life could be traced back to that day when the British fleet captured Lucien Bonaparte. From then on when anything went wrong my father would curse that fated day, saying how it would have been if we had only gone to the New World and made a vast fortune instead of living a simple life as the subject of a king and his earls and lords who were still all powerful in this land and could only be removed by a revolution.

'What this country needs is a good day's shooting', was his favourite saying, and my mother because she was more of a republican than him would add, 'It'll take a week'.

So I can go back 200 years, which is not long, there are families here in south Shropshire that have their names in the Doomsday book, but I have been here longer than the fare that I have in the taxi at this moment. A Brummie Admiral and his wife, they have been in the town less than two years but think they own it.

It is such a shame for them. They have come here from the most ugly city in Europe, perhaps because of that they are visually ignorant. But they have money which proves that anyone can make money. So, armed with a pile of wonga that they gathered by fair means or foul they have been let loose on a once beautiful old barn that never did anyone any harm in the first place. The wife is a predatory animal wearing a Wonder Bra. For the last half hour she has been telling me about how they did all the work themselves and saved thousands on the project.

'Yow ave no idea how it feels to see a project through from planning ...' I hate the way they say yow instead of you

Sentences like that, dull boring sentences, and all the time I've been saying, 'Oh really, yes, you have done well' or just grunting back at them because he is drunk and I can understand why London taxi cabs have divisions ...

'She is very good, yow know, she watches them. We had a carpenter, well, he called himself that, and he used to get here at eight thirty. Said that he wanted travelling time, well, I ain't payin' him travelling time ...'

And I have to listen to this Admiral rabbiting away, me an ex bricklayer driving a cab because the nine inch concrete blocks gave me three hernias and this salt is telling me about his barn conversion and I know the carpenter who he never paid and then I'm at the beginning of the drive in front of a five bar gate.

'It's electric. I got a clicker ...'

And the man pulls from his pocket a thing like a TV clicker and he aims it at the gate, and we wait and sure enough the latch lifts and the thing starts to move open and his wife leans towards him and I look straight ahead because she has a cleavage that looks as if it's been around too long, about as attractive as the udders on our old Border Collie bitch ... not true, the dog's more attractive, at least she's a Christian. The only religion that these have is Greed, Greed, Greed. It takes a long time for the gate to open and so I push forward before it completely opens just in case the Admiral wants to repeat the procedure because he is crazy about his electric gates and then there is another opening, this time with a cattle grid and then I see the barn conversion and it looks like what it is, a converted barn done like all the others with a slate roof with eight Velux windows ...

'Living room with inglenook fireplace, patio doors leading onto a rear garden and five bedrooms, three with en suite bathrooms ...'

Wonder Bra is telling me all this. It's as if she has memorised the details from an estate agent's leaflet. I'm thinking just the two of them, but of course it's not a home, it's an asset and will fetch three hundred thousand ... because it's got a swimming pool ... and I'm trying to picture Wonder Bra in that pool out the back with the Clee hill behind and the Brummie with the clicker in his hand because they've got a great satellite disc, but no bookshelves because they can't read, these are truly ignorant people ... I feel sick, and try to figure out how I can fiddle the fare but I can't because he phoned for a quote ...

'There are three things in this life that are forever,' I tell the Brummie as he pays, 'Death, Taxes and the Law of Pataphysics,' and he looks at me with a vacant empty look and I give him no change from the tenner.

As I do my turn I try to figure out who could afford to live in the dump because there just are not any jobs around here that pay enough money for a local to even dream about living in a converted barn, not that a local would want to anyway. I mean barns have been lying empty for years.

As I drive away into the night my thoughts worry me somewhat. Perhaps the Brummie Admiral knows more than I do.

# 3   *The German Prisoner*

As I drive away from the Brummie Admiral and his wife Wonder Bra, I think about numbers and how as I've grown older the numbers have got longer so that a quarter of a million pounds is not very much and how when Dad used to do the pools his only dream was to win seventy-five thousand so that he could live the rest of his life without working at the gasworks ... and now you can't even buy a decent house for that amount. Of course, it is all relative to what it was back then, just a few more noughts.

All of a sudden I have the urge to drive down the narrow lane that leads to the level crossing where my father caught the German. It's stupid because I know that the crossing is not there any more, there is no need for it, a new road runs in a cutting where the crossing used to be. Not many people know that there was a road from Steventon to Ashford on the other side of the river. I used to go down there with an old bike wheel, just the rim, my hoop. I hit it with a stick and as it rolled along it became a truck and my dog ran with me and there was a spring that tasted of salt. Once an old man who was ditching told me that they used to collect the water from that spring in milk churns and take it to Hereford hospital.

'Some said that they used to take it on the train

to Shrewsbury hospital as well,' he said. 'I never seen um do that, but I did see um put it on a cart and they told me it was going to Hereford. It was good for the gout, they said.'

That spring came out of the ground at a place called Saltmore which isn't there any more. There is a road on top of it. To get an idea of how it once was you have to approach from Ashford. You have to go down a lane that has a sign that says No Through Road.

The lane seems narrower now than it did. It is unused, brambles brush the sides of the car. I try to visualise what the lane was like just before it crosses the track. There should be a turning point. There used to be a small holding that butted onto the crossing house. I used to know a girl who lived somewhere near that house, she used to go to my school. I have a photo of our class holding pets. She's holding one of my rabbits because it was too far for her to walk with her cat. She used to walk two miles to school each day. She had a long pigtail. I used to dip it in the ink well.

The lane gets narrower. I am afraid that I shall have to reverse back and the reversing light is knackered, this taxi having covered three hundred thousand miles, almost as many noughts as the Brummies want for their barn.

Fear

There is no need to be afraid, but the lane goes further than I remember, it's been extended into a quarry. It seems that the people now living in the crossing house are using the stone from the quarry to build an extension. There's stone everywhere, and rubble from the flank end wall, rusted scaffolding, cement bags, concrete blocks, three old oil drums, next to an old cement mixer with a tarp over it. A pile of 4 × 2s and old oak beams. It looks as if a bomb's landed. Now I am afraid. Afraid as only an old tradesman can be when he sees what happens when idiots are let loose on a site. I reverse the car and the headlights scroll into the black night. No sign of life, no one about, deserted. It looks as if the bank has pulled the rug from under it. I move well away.

The night is still. It is very dark. I am afraid of the dark. I am so urban that I have great difficulty in dealing with the dark. I once went poaching in complete darkness. I kept running into things. The poachers were country people who were used to the dark. I was happy when the moon came out, they were not. They were good poachers, I was not. They had a sense that I have lost.

I am completely disoriented. There is a hedge to the left of me and on my right a forest. I have a feeling that the railway line is up on an embankment, but it isn't, it's below me.

The twin tracks are still there but where the lane went the other side of the railway, there is a road, a main road. It is the bypass that goes round our town, an altered state, another landscape.

I walk across the field down towards the railway line. There is the sound of cars swishing by. It seems that the sounds on the road are held and reflected back down onto me as I walk across the hollow that is in the centre of the field. The sound decreases as I reach the railway.

Looking up towards the town's orange street lights I see a truck with green lights over its cab and four headlights sweeping the road in front of it. I see it before I hear the sound of its wheels rolling along the tarmac. And then just as the sound disappears the railway lines start humming, it's almost a

sizzling sound, steel running on steel, a new sound
… just before a great diesel locomotive pulling a
freight train comes from the opposite direction to
the truck, out of the night.

This place is nothing like it was when my Dad saw
the German plane crash land and then caught the
pilot. The train would have made a different sound
back then. He would have heard steam trains.

I was conditioned from an early age to the sound
of steam trains. I was born in the steam age. This
line runs at the top of what used to be my garden.

The best time to hear steam trains is on crisp cold
frosty mornings when you can hear the locomotive's
exhaust beat like a sharp bark. I could hear this
bark five miles away, a cannonade escaping from
the deep cutting, a sonata of sounds prepared for
steam engine and trucks as they tumbled over each
other, the trucks in desperate pursuit as they passed
my window at the top of the garden, the whole train
leaving behind a decaying echo as it went into the
tunnel and then the interlude of bird song hanging
from the apple trees before a Down Express … and
if I went beneath the sheets then there was nothing
but the sound of my heart pumping, the deep puls-
ing of my blood, me a separate existence growing
slowly into a boyman.

Every morning the same awakening and always at
a quarter to eight my father slurping his final cup of
tea, placing it back in the saucer just as the eight
forty-five Goods came out of the cutting.

But one morning there was something wrong
with the fragments of sound. That final cup of tea
was missing. It was as if a note had been removed
from the symphony.

That morning fifty years ago, I sat up. And heard
his bike as he leant it against the wall. My Dad was

coming home when he should be going out to work.

Moving quickly from my bed, I descended the stairs and entered the room at the same time as he did, him in his Home Guards uniform, carrying his four-ten shotgun, and his boots with the studs that held the dirt that my mother hated, scraping across the Ruabon tiled floor.

'We caught a Jerry,' Dad said and my mother laughed at him. It was a closed laugh that formed between her closed lips, and all the time she grinned she folded her hands in the bottom of her apron.

'We did,' he said again, and he sighed a tired sigh and I saw him stumble a little like he sometimes did when he'd had too much cider. And I saw that mother had seen him stumble. She missed nothing.

'Ummmph, you'll want to think of something else,' she said, 'you have to be at work in ten minutes.'

Work ... that was the word, the Protestant work ethic stamped from birth into the deepest recess of our brains. A good day's work for a good day's pay. Dad and Mum both believed in work and there was nothing in the world that should get in the way of it. Even illness was frowned upon and we had a doctor whose only prescription was medicine and work, if you could walk you went to work or school.

I once had tonsils so big that they met in the middle, but I could walk. I went to school and I suffered.

'It will pass,' Mother used to say. 'Pain is only a feeling, it will pass.'

It did pass but I would have rather been in bed. I never missed a day's schooling in my life. I very rarely get ill. It is something to say at the end of the day. The day of reckoning, that last day when somebody will total up your life, when you hand in the

27

book, when the whole of your life has been spent working, earning an honest living and we must not be found wanting. So that when we die no one can say that he was afraid of a day's work.

That was what we were brought up to believe.

I remember one day my Dad going to see Mr (doctor) Hunter. You called him Mister because he was a surgeon. Dad had a pain in his side so Mr Hunter told him to go up to the hospital and see matron and ask her to put him in one of his beds. All the doctors had their own beds, they had their names on them. And Mister Hunter did the cutting. He told Dad that he would be up with his knife, he said that he thought that Dad had appendicitis. Dad never went up, instead he made a miraculous recovery.

Those were the days when the cottage hospital was run by a matron for the local doctors, strict visiting hours, two to a bed, all leaving when the bell was rung, open wide, breakfast at five thirty, doctor knows best.

Mr Hunter's partner had a glass-backed bee hive in the French window of his surgery in Broad Street. There was a printed notice on the mantel piece:

'One hundred pounds reward if you can find a bee-keeper with rheumatism'.

He used bees as a remedy. He used to sting patients with bees and they came from miles around, paying dearly for the experience. There used to be chauffeur driven limousines down both sides of the street. Bent double the patients went in and because they believed the treatment worked, or perhaps because they were so afraid of the doctor, they walked out upright.

Work was so important that you could be given

twelve months hard labour for not working. There was one amongst our number who had been continually late for work for six months. His excuse was that he had a bad leg and could not run for the bus that took him to the armaments factory at Peaton. The charge against him was that he was hindering the war effort by being late for work. After the expert opinion of Doctor Fenton who proclaimed that there was nothing wrong with him he was sentenced to three months hard labour in Shrewsbury Jail, and that was only for being late. God only knows what he would have got if he had refused to work. The magistrate would have probably had him transported to Mars.

But after work, the beliefs of my mother and father went in separate directions. Dominoes, cider drinking, horse racing, playing jazz, whilst at the same time telling stories or jokes, were Dad's pastimes, whilst mother, a Baptist who had signed the pledge, never allowed alcohol to pass her lips. For her, even the eating of Christmas pudding if it had even the smallest amount of brandy added was not permitted. She had her violin and Mozart and she was a pacifist. They were so opposite that I wondered how they had ever got married. In fact, for years I thought that marriage meant that Dads had a garden shed and Mums had a house.

'We caught a Jerry,' Dad said.

And Mum said, 'That's a lot of silly fool's talk, you couldn't catch a cold. If Hitler only knew that this country was defended by idiots carrying broomsticks and shotguns and if them up Sheet Road at the prisoners of war camp knew that, then they could just get up and walk away from it all.'

'They got nowhere to go to,' Dad said. 'Them up on the Sheet are beat.'

And I thought about all the Germans and Italians up in the prisoner of war camp behind the wire fence, dressed in their tattered uniforms, and I was glad that my Dad was my Dad and that we were English and that we were not beat.

And then there was silence. And I thought that for a moment my Dad would get up and walk out, but he couldn't do that, he was still in his uniform and what was more he had not had his tea and he had to drink two cups at least before he could even move out of the house. He was a great drinker, was my Dad. He had a fear, an obsession, that he had to keep his system continually flushed. So I knew that he would have to have his tea. And so I made my way to the sofa, put my chin on the leather back and felt the dog rest her muzzle on my bare feet.

'Well,' Dad began.

And then my mother walked away. She had to light the gas under the boiler that heated the water for the washing. She would do things like that to save time so that by the time Dad had finished talking at least the water would be warming, or perhaps she did it to see how far she could go, leaving him there with his word hanging in the air.

So Dad began again. 'There were the two of us,' he said, 'and we were guarding that level crossing at Ashford. Boneyard Johnson and me. And I was sayin' to him the stupidness of it all, us havin' to work all day and do soldierin' at night so that there were times in a week when we never slept for more than forty-eight hours and we were about to decide which one of us would go and sleep up there in the barn which was just filled with hay and a nice smell it was too, when we heard the plane. Well, Boneyard's dog heard it first. A drone, it was.'

'They let you take a dog on guard duty?' Mother said.

'Boneyard's dog goes everywhere Boneyard goes and Boneyard goes everywhere his dog goes,' my Dad said, 'and there is nothing the army or anyone else can do about it, it is a fact of life.'

As Dad said the word 'fact' he lifted his mug and drank and I watched his Adam's apple move up and down.

And then he replaced the cup and said that they both heard sort of an uncontrolled drone, 'like as if the engine was missin', Dad said it was, 'like if there was no fuel gettin through, it was like as if it was coming out of the hill. A great black shadow,' he said it was, 'so low that plane was that it hit the telephone wires on the side of the railway and they stretched out before they broke so that it was like violin strings breaking and then there was the whoosh through the air after they broke. Wooooosssh,' he said, and he lifted his arm in the air. 'Wooooosssh.' He sliced his arm through the air so that all I saw was a blur.

'If we'd been nearer then we'd ave been cut in half, like cheese wires, they were'. And my Dad said that it was deadly, and all the undercarriage of the plane was ripped off so that nuts and bolts peppered down and that him and Boneyard were watching it right up to the moment when it swooped lower making a creaking sound as it ripped into the top of the distance signal just before a train came past.

'A goods train, it was,' Dad said, 'and I counted the trucks as they passed,' he said, 'nine, ten, eleven, twelve, right up to thirty-eight and then the guard's van like a little hut went past and its red light swinging and all the time me saying thirty-eight

31

like a part of measured time that had been counted, but had stopped.'

And when the train passed Dad said that it became silent. 'It was as if all the sound had gone, had disappeared with the train. It was an empty coal train', Dad said it was, 'and there is nothing like a train of empty trucks moving just a few feet away from you and slowing down for a distant signal that is no longer there. It makes one hell of a noise does an empty train. But when that train had gone the silence hurt our ears'.

When the train had gone Dad said that Boneyard said, 'It's bloody well landed'.

'There is no need to use that language,' Mother said.

'That was what Boneyard said, his words,' Dad said. 'And then we both moved to the other side of the railway line and we saw the plane. It was not more than fifty yards away, there it was, so silent and the moon came out and it really was a German plane.'

'Did it have a swastika on it?' I asked.

'No,' Dad said. 'A big black cross.'

And Dad said that Boneyard said, 'Bugger this for a lark, I ain't gonna be a hero holdin' this er broomstick and a planeload o'Jerries comes out.'

But Dad and Boneyard never moved.

'We never moved,' Dad said. 'We were sort of held there, lookin at it.'

And there was only one way for whoever was in the plane to go and that was towards Dad and Boneyard, the river being between the plane and the main road, and so Dad said to Boneyard:

'Let's hide in the barn and wait.'

'Good idea,' he replied. 'And then if they are armed, we can run into town and warn the regulars who have real guns, and who would not be warned if we was to die in the apprehension of the enemy, thereby we be savin' lives and might get a medal.'

'Right,' my Dad said.

And so they quietly went into the barn which was full of hay and they climbed up to the top and could see the plane lying there, a great black shadow.

'You would think that a plane would be a big thing, but it ain't much bigger than a bus,' Dad said.

And so they waited for a long time, knowing that if there was any one in that plane then they would have to come towards them.

'And the longer we waited the more we got used to it,' Dad said. 'And then as we were deciding to take a closer look, we saw the mon, like a shadow. It was him. It was the Jerry walking towards us on the other side of the level crossing. And then he stood there and Boneyard said, "He's waitin' fer a train". Which was not that daft a thing to do when you think that a goods train is only going at fifteen miles an hour and it would be a simple thing to take a ride. Well, a train did come and it was a Goods, movin' slowly.'

Boneyard said: 'Shoot him afore he gets on the train'.

And then my Dad started to laugh. 'It would'na have killed him, a four ten shotgun uld ave peppered him and perhaps goaded him into jumpin' on the train, so I never even lifted the gun and I thanked God that Boneyard had only his broomstick, because I think that he would have shot him jead.'

And then my Dad shook his head and you could see that he was thinking about what he would have felt if he had shot the German.

'Well,' Dad said, 'the train went past and the Jerry was still there.'

'Wait fer him to get near and then shoot him,' Boneyard said.

'I can't just shoot him,' Dad said.

'Why not?' Boneyard said.

'We gotta say "Halt, who goes there?" first,' Dad said.

'Bollocks to that,' said Boneyard, 'and then as you says "Friend or foe?" he pulls out his gun and shoots yer and then when he sees me holdin' a broomstick, he shoots me, cause if he says foe, which is what he will say because he is a foe, then you gotta shoot him, so you might as well let him ave it in the first place and anyway he ain't gonna understand a word you says to him.'

My Dad was laughing again and he said that he'd thought about what Boneyard said and almost did what he said because he was afraid and then he saw in his mind's eye what a rabbit does when you shoot it and how it squeals and falls over on its side and then he said that he realised that he could not shoot a mon.

'Not then, not ever could I shoot a mon,' he said.

And Dad reached out towards his cup of tea which was steaming and he added three sugars to it, stirred and then he drank half of it down and my mother looked at him and went to him and placed her cheek on his and I realised that there was nothing else that he would have done and then my father started to laugh, it was as if he was relieved of the unexpected calamity.

And then he said, 'So I just walked out of that barn and I walked up to the Jerry and I said to him, "You'd better come uth me".'

That was what my Dad said to the German, and

34

my Dad said that the German never said a word, he just stopped in his tracks and it was dark and he couldn't see him, just his dark form standing there.

'It was so quiet,' my Dad said, 'it was as if my words had stamped on all the sources of sound' … and then my Dad said that the German started to squeal like a pig.

'At first I couldn't make out why,' Dad said, 'and then I saw that Boneyard was poking him with his broomstick and his dog was snapping at the German's legs and I was yelling at Boneyard to stop. The daft bastard, that was all I wanted, a mad Jerry who could have had a pistol and might have made a run for it and that was when I realised that there was no cartridges in the gun. I'd left the cartridges at home and I was yellin' at Boneyard to stop shovin' his broomstick up the Jerry's arse when a train came down towards us and no one could hear anything and the Jerry was holding his hands over his head with Boneyard's broomstick hovering over him, so I clouted Boneyard with the stock of the gun and Boneyard went down holding his ribcage and all the time his dog was snapping at me and the Jerry …'

'And so,' my Dad said, 'when the train finally disappeared down the line Boneyard was groaning and rolling on the ground like a mad bear and trying to hold onto the Jerry's leg and gibbering, "You bastard, you kicked me in the gut." Which was not a bad thing, him thinking that the Jerry had hit him. But the Jerry stepped to one side and said in perfect English:

"Here, call off the dog."

"Call the dog," I shouted to Boneyard.

But Boneyard was still on the floor and the dog was leaping around at me and the German, so we ran, the German and me ran down the lane with Boneyard's dog after us and then Boneyard called the dog and me and the German stopped running and turned and I said:

"Sorry about that, that dog is a bastard."

"English terrier," the German said.

"Good ratter," I said, "but uncontrollable."

'And he gave me his pistol and as he gave it to me he unloaded it and then he held it out handle first so that I took it correctly and I could tell that the Jerry was a gentleman which was more than can be said for Boneyard, who could not find his broomstick … Look here.'

And my Dad unbuttoned his uniform and pulled out the pistol that he'd taken from the German. It was a single action striker, a self-loader, a Luger, and the handle was brown polished, all shining and deadly and my Dad took it from a German.

'Take it back,' my mother said.

'How can I do that?'

'Take it back, I don't want that thing in the house.'

'I can't take it back.'

'You stole it.'

'Removed it.'

'It's still stealing.'

'All right, I'll have to tell them that I'd forgot.'

But Dad never gave the gun back. Instead he filled the barrel with lead and kept it in the shed.

And that was how Dad caught the German. But what happened next was even better and a touch of genius on my Dad's part because the German was no ordinary German. This German had before the war been part of an exchange scheme changing places with a Grammar school boy from the other side of Bucknell, who had lived with his family in

Germany. He told Dad this while they smoked beside the level crossing and so my Dad said to the German:

'Let's go,' and he took the German onto the main road and told Boneyard to stop the next car. Which they did, Dad pointing his shotgun at the car and then they told the driver to drive them to the Army camp. But the driver only had enough petrol to drive into town. So they got out at the bridge and woke Mrs Rogers up at the Wheatsheaf.

I'll never forget what Dad said about the German, 'He weren't a bad bloke,' he said, 'he could sink a pint like a good un.'

And so they phoned the army at Bromfield and they waited until six in the morning for them to come and pick the German up.

'It was a hell of a thing,' Dad said. 'He'd got English money on him but Mrs Rogers said it was forged and she wouldn't accept payment and we had to act sober when the Army came so Mrs Rogers took the Jerry upstairs to wash a cut on his face and we, me and Boneyard, slept on the floor, and this is the best part, when the Army came the captain started to shout his mouth and Bill Rogers told him that he would bar him if he didn't shut up and was going to slam the door in his face but the German walked out into the street and I winked at the German and he winked back at me.'

And I remembered it all, the tale and how it changed every time it was told. Once the story was a living thing that faded away when it wasn't told anymore. So that after all those years it became a legend to the few people who knew or had knowledge of it.

Trapped in the landscape in between buildings where we live are thousands of images, faded stories trying to emerge, unable to leave, trapped perhaps for a thousand years or maybe for ever until released by memories, me smoking a cigarette in the middle of the night leaning on the gates of an old level crossing remembering how half the town went out to look at the plane which was guarded by the Americans who had a base not a mile away and how the citizens of our town were coming back from the plane saying that the Yanks were there and some of them were pulling empty wheelbarrows because they were unable to loot the plane, they could not plunder the sheet metal and how they were scuffing the earth with their heels looking for nuts so that they might have a souvenir but all had been scavenged, all those bits that had peppered down were gone so that the only thing that we had was the fact that Dad had captured the German.

It is strange to think that a plane could have landed where the bypass now runs, but it would be a stranger thing if sometime in the future a motorist were to see it sitting there, a transparent ghost, an imprint captured in a vehicle's headlights for a split second, something from the swarm of transparent garbage now materialising out of a digitized world ... but since the pilot did not die but instead drank a few beers with my Dad then perhaps the spirits will have no need to tell us that it happened at all.

# 4 *Fat of the Land*

The B4078 runs into the A49 just before you get to the second bridge in our town. It is the sort of road that smacks of the past. It twists and turns through common land underneath a few remaining oak trees, the rest having been mown down and burnt, the Forestry Commission's successful metamorphosing of our forest from broad leaves into pine needles.

When I was young I came up here one night looking for glow worms. Each side of the road used to be illuminated with the miniature phosphorescent glowing from their little bums. I took home a jam jar of grass and about a dozen worms, freeing them on the side of the railway embankment, thinking that I might be able to encourage them to breed and so illuminate my beloved railway line with twinkling lights. Of course I killed them, an open railway embankment being as unsuitable a place as any for a glow worm to live. Just as unsuitable for the poor little things as a pine forest.

So now there are none.

If you follow this road, as I did last week in my taxi cab, you go past a ramshackle farm; barns with corrugated iron roofs, and you will eventually come to a sign saying, 'Walcome Hall Farm. B&B'.

It also says underneath, 'Camping, High teas, Light lunches, and Evening meal'.

You'll cross a courtyard beset with fountains and strange garden ornaments of little boys pissing into ponds and then there is a farm shop, full of jams and local honey and more signs pointing towards concrete paths and pens with African pygmy goats, ducks, chickens, cockerels, pigs. The whole converges onto a great barn with a massive lean-to conservatory attached.

Inside you'll find home-made cakes and Shrewsbury biscuits, various quiches and ploughman's lunches with a side salad that you may dress in salad dressings of mustard and garlic and mayonnaise, or just salad cream, meals that will cost a day's pay, and you may have lentil and thyme soup, lemon and lime cookies or a chocolate fudge slice, coffee sponge or perhaps a chocolate orange-chip shortcake.

This is a tourist hovel. This place is a real find, this is what the countryside has become at the end of the 20th Century. Caterers to the carriage trade. The carriages backed up beside each other, a red Ferrari next to an aluminium Audi, a brace of BMW's, great Volvo estates, people carriers and an old Morris 1000 with traces of skin cancer and a for sale sign stuck on the rear window asking £3000 for something that cost less than a grand thirty years ago.

Knee deep in coffee sponge cake, a fat man, big-boned with skin like a turkey's neck, so full of his own ego that he wears an open-necked shirt that says, 'If you are as important and as rich as I am, then and only then you can afford to molest the creature opposite me,' who is picking at a bowl of lentil and thyme soup.

That was the small table. Around the large one, four people, two men and two women, sitting talking, sentences prompted by large laughter that was bigger than the magnum of Moet floating at an angle in a steel bucket, an old milking pail that had been improvised and filled with ice, in the centre of the remains of plates once full of meringue and clotted cream.

'What you don't know won't hurt you,' one of the men said. He was wearing jogging pants and a large silver crucifix over a white T-shirt.

'And what you do is killing you dead,' the woman opposite him said.

She was wearing large black dark sunglasses high on the top of her head, a yellow sleeveless sweatshirt and a smile that was more than half way across her face. Both women were smiling. They had peppermint smiles and the one nearest to where I was standing had long legs squeezed into a pair of velvet hot pants held up by a brown leather belt just below her navel. Her navel was ringed with a gold ring.

'So I'll probably leave the plage wear,' she said. 'I'll pack some sacks instead. The pale look is back.'

The women were not as drunk as they should have been. Perhaps they were used to it.

'Taxi,' I said and stood waiting.

'Ah, the taxi,' the other man said. He was dark-skinned Mediterranean, a Greek or perhaps French. 'It's manslaughter,' he said to the crucifix and then to me he said, 'We want coffee', and a long pause before he said: 'You'll wait.'

'The meter is running,' I said and I turned and walked back to the cab.

Outside swifts were darting across the sky and then something jumped from a garden chair, a large grey cat lifting a long quivering tail. It rubbed against my legs. It was the sanest thing for miles around and could have been descended from the cats that used to infest this place when I came up here with my father when the entrance was a rutted lane that only a horse and cart or tractor could negotiate. That was when the clapboard-faced barn had double doors leading down into a cellar where there used to be more than a dozen cider barrels fermenting away, where we used to come once every fortnight for six gallons of sweet medium that looked like fog when poured.

My mother never got over the fact that Dad was a cider drinker and that every two weeks he would have to refill his precious six gallon barrel, that every other Saturday morning he would clean out that barrel. Then the backyard would become full of cider smells and the dog restless, going round in ever decreasing circles until we were ready to move off, Uncle Dicky riding 'Walter Raleigh', with me on his cross bar, sitting on a strapped on cushion holding the handle bars and Dad the six gallon barrel in the front carrier, the three of us moving, cycling through town stopping twice, once to buy a large white loaf and then again for a pound of cheese.

Saturday afternoon, fifty years ago, cycling towards the hill and then we walked beneath the oak trees, pushing the bikes because it was steep and all the time the dog covering the road ahead. Until we got to that part of the road that was level enough to tramp on the pedals, Uncle Dicky and Dad with all the weight of their bodies, me holding on to the handlebars, feeling Uncle Dicky's heartbeats, him always ahead of Dad, Sir Walter Raleigh boasting a 'Sturmey Archer Three Speeds' that would sometimes miss and then Uncle Dicky would push me forward, pulling me back with his right arm once he had regained his momentum after having spat three yards ahead of us on the road.

It was incredible, those men's constitutions. When they stopped to rest they would roll fags and then suck deeply, filling their lungs, and then when they exhaled the air around us hung with fine digested smoke, and then the sound of heavy breathing and free spitting where they stood resting, the dog smelling and lifting his leg and you never saw a car going up the road from Wigmore to Ludlow.

They had strange conversations.

'On with the motley,' my father would shout.

'To eternity,' Uncle Dicky would shout back.

'The end is nigh.'

'Work.'

'Do not mention that word.'

'Who invented work?'

And then my father would start to explain how it was that the introduction of slavery had brought into disrepute the idea of manual labour and Uncle Dicky would listen in silence for a while until he shouted something like,

'Is this the road to eternity?'

'It could be,' Dad would shout, and then one of them would shout:

'But there is no sign post.'

And then they would check the clips on their trousers before they mounted in unison, Uncle Dicky scooping me up with his right arm and my father by now ahead but Uncle Dicky catching up because of his three speeds. And then we all rode down into the yard watched by birds conversing in the branches of the great horse chestnut tree that sheltered from the sun a herd of cows who were examining the morning's eating, bit by bit unhurryingly, heads hardly moving, all of them looking as if they understood the enjoyments of the world.

And then when Ebenezer's dog met our dog, Ebenezer would shout 'You lousy odd thing you' and our dog would piss and then Ebenezer's dog would smell our dog's bum and Ebenezer would come out of the cider barn, always wearing a brown tweed jacket over blue overalls that he wore over grey flannel trousers. Ebenezer Price had never been seen dressed in any other apparel. Winter and summer the same and the same old cheesecutter hat that was black-peaked and greasy with age and the short stumpy pipe that was removed from his mouth only to drink cider or to eat or perhaps sleep.

'That uld hill gets steeper every time,' Dad would shout, and Ebenezer would shout back:

'But think what it'll be like goin' back.'

And then he would look at Uncle Dicky and he would say, 'Looks like Richard's brought Sir Walter Raleigh.'

Each time almost the same conversations.

Inside that barn there were brown twisted wires holding one clear light bulb that was covered in brown fly stain and there was an identical one in the cellar. There were no glasses, just a collection of cows' horns and Ebenezer would wash them under the pump with his hands that were great hard-worked paws with the texture of a worn dog's pad. His nails were black so that you never knew whether the washing made the glasses cleaner or dirtier than they were before. And then he would ask Dad what kind of cider he would like to try and Uncle Dicky and Dad would start the tasting .

'To the future,' Dad would shout.

'To eternity,' Uncle Dicky shouted.

'By gum, this is good tack.'

'You have excelled yourself. By God, Ebenezer, there's a spider's web on the top' and Dad was holding his horn so that we could all see the shape on the top of his drink and then he would hold it up and shout, 'To Pataphysics and the law of imaginary solutions'.

'What's that, Jack?' Ebenezer would sometimes ask.

'A science on the one hand and reality on the other,' Dad would respond.

And then Dad drank the cider down in one deep draft and I thought that I could hear the liquid running down into his stomach like water going down a drainpipe, and then Uncle Dicky did the same and then they were onto the next barrel that was called Sweet Medium and Ebenezer gave me a horn that was full of the sweet kind. But it was not that sweet-tasting, it sort of made my teeth ache a little and it travelled down to my legs. It was quite nice but made my legs weak, so I used to have to sit down on an old bench.

By now they were moving towards a barrel that was called 'Bread and Cheese' cider.

'You'll want some bread and cheese to eat uth this, Jack,' Ebenezer said and Dad said that he'd got some and sent me out to get it from the saddlebag of Uncle Dicky's bike. I brought the pound of cheese in as well. Dad asked old Ebenezer where he could cut it, and was told to put it on the old saw bench.

The saw bench was always dirty, but one of them would just brush the dust away. It was amazing the amount of dirt that we got into each other back then, and we were never ill from it. I often think now, that had a public health hygiene officer ever seen how we ate and drank back in the good old days then we would all have been put away in some isolation hospital.

Ebenezer said that Dad would have to be careful of the Bread and Cheese cider, 'It goes through yer,' he said. 'It's more medicinal … more a tonic than a drink.'

'We'll try just a tad,' Dad said.

And when it was drawn from the barrel there was a vapour evaporating from its surface which seemed to come from a white scum that looked like the spider's web floating on the liquid.

'It has qualities of a strange uplifting nature,' Dad said. 'It will fortify the stomach', and Dad coughed after he'd swallowed a mouthful.

'It'll go right through yer,' Uncle Dicky said. 'Jesus,' he said. 'It's got the taste of a shepherdess's knickers.'

I watched them sipping and then Dad cut the bread and they all took a slice of cheese, placing the cheese on the bread and then they were cutting and eating with their pen knives and they all left thumb prints on the cheese but they ate with great appetites, and sometimes old Ebenezer would find some shallots and those shallots were sweet, almost like fruit. Then if there was a silence they would break it by farting or belching, sometimes a giant blue bottle buzzed around the cellar looking at us.

'I'd better have the Medium,' Dad would say.

And Old Ebenezer would take an old rubber tube from a nail and push it onto the wooden tap on the Medium barrel and then he rolled Dad's barrel into position and I listened to it filling, the sound changing as the barrel filled, Dad and Uncle Dicky sipping away and Ebenezer topping up the cows' horns so that they were continually filled, seducing the holder into drink.

And that's how it normally was, every other Saturday afternoon the same and if you went along that road by accident, like taking the dog for a walk or looking for chestnuts or if you went looking for walnuts then sometimes you might see others coming from Ebenezer's Cider Mill, pulling a cart made of old pram wheels or a wheel barrow. Old Bill Downes from the bike shop had a tandem with a fitted sidecar which he used to fetch a barrel in. A fine thing, Dad said it was. He wanted to buy that tandem. He and Uncle Dicky reckoned that they could get to Aberystwyth and back on one filling.

So that's how it was, every one going about their business with a tenacity that was strong because of the war.

One Saturday however there was a change. This was when they put the Clydesdale stallion to the mare. We came round the corner that afternoon and there was nobody there. Ebenezer was nowhere about. All we could hear was a neighing in the field beyond the orchard and then Ebenezer's dog, having a higher sense of smell than the others, came round the barn and smelt our dog's bum and then both animals ran off round the back to where they was a neighing and a whinnying and then the thundering of hooves, a rattling of chains a jingling of buckles and Ebenezer was shouting,

'HEY THERE WHOA, COME BOY COME … EASY'

And as we came round the corner to the gate between the field and the orchard we saw the stallion with huge steel shoes on his hairy feet. We saw those steel shoes shining because his feet were above the five bar gate. It was as if he was trying to crawl over it, and Mrs Ebenezer, who had hands that were almost as big as her husband's, was pulling on the harness of the mare, trying to get the mare's backside towards the gate but the mare was furiously bobbing about, that mare who weighed more than two tons was harnessed with leather buckles and straps pulled round so that Ebenezer's wife was almost lifted off her feet and then both horses bit at each other's necks, the stallion having got down from the gate was banging that gate so that both of them were banging simultaneously and alternately and the stallion's dick seemed to grow longer so that it was almost dragging the ground and then constantly in that movement the two horses seemed to gather a mutual understanding, puffs of breath rolling from their nostrils and the whites of their eyes showing so that as she moved her backside towards the gate, her hooves shifting a handful of stones, sparking like flints, and the stallion, all two tons of him, desperately trying to place his dick. The land girl who was eighteen years old, who had been jumping about, almost out of sight, her breasts bobbing up and down inside her loose blouse, did not know what to do until Ebenezer shouted out loud for her to place the stallion's tool into the correct place.

'PUT HIS DICK IN HER,' he shouted.

And so the land girl, who came from Liverpool, had to lean under that horse, her with her breasts swinging like bells in a church tower, and she took hold of that great tool and then the mare's eyes started rolling and every muscle in every part of the bodies of those two great animals took on a new life so that there was a speeding up of things and the stallion was sweating and both the eyes of those animals were rolling as they remembered that there was something else besides hay and oats and then the animals developed a mutual understanding, coming together so that when Ebenezer shouted 'WHOA ... WHOOOOOOOOA' the stallion's great tool slipped out, and the horse gently got down from the gate and seemed almost weak as Ebenezer threw a couple of buckets of water over the mare's backside whilst at the same time shouting to the land girl to take the stallion away and rub him down with straw and then came the sound of the whinnying of the mare and Uncle Dicky said to my Dad:

'Her can rub me down any time.'

# 5    *The Lion of Judea*

On the first Sunday in every month my father used to cut the graves. That is how it was. Everybody did the same, there were no overgrown cemeteries in those days and if someone's family had died out because they'd emigrated or some other tragedy overcame the family, then those graves were still cut.

'Poor Miss Hudson,' my father said. 'Er was a good uld stick, brother in Ceylon, tea picker, well, manager, I suppose, good uld Tory, never done any hard work ... well, we'd better cut er hair.'

And so I took the small ladies' shears and snipped away between the stone borders of Miss Hudson's grave that was two away from Aunt Emma's. My shears cut well. They were sharp. Dad had sharpened them in the shed the night before.

My father's shed was at the top of the garden right at the bottom of the railway embankment. If you were in Dad's shed when a train went by then you would hear each individual wheel roll across the joints and if the distant signal was up and it was a goods train then as that train slowed down the buffers of the trucks would collide one with the other and as the engine passed our shed it would whistle in grievance and then more than likely it would get the road and all those trucks would shudder in protest as the slack couplings became stretched so that you waited for that chain of trucks to snap at the weakest link, such a ferocious rattling that sometimes you ran outside the shed and looked up, but all that happened was that the train rattled by and if you ran up that embankment as the leaves were falling then you would see a leaf storm gathering behind the vanishing guard's van.

Dad spent half his spare time in that shed. It had a proper pitched tiled roof. All the battens were visible from inside, you could see the fingers of the tiles holding on to those battens and in between them were black spiders' webs. Dad liked spiders, 'Clean creatures,' he called them. There was a great black stove along the back wall and in the far corner was a giant refrigerator. This was gas powered, with a flame, a blue flame solitary and lonely, not much bigger than a candle's flame, but blue. The flame that cooled … The lamps too were gas. I liked those lamps.

Last night, as my Dad had sharpened the shears in the shed, I'd watched his hands moving in the light of those burning hissing lamps. As his hands had pushed the file across the blades all the shadows in his shed were monsters dancing.

I'd drunk cider with my father last night. Dad always gave me plenty of cider. 'It won't hurt yer,' he used to say, 'Good honest tack, pure apple juice.' And so I drank it from the time I was a baby, when Mother used to leave me with Dad so that she could study at the workers educational association. From the first time Dad filled the bottle with cider I wanted more because I used to drift away, quietly, sleeping, peaceful.

Watching Dad and whatever Dad did in his shed was always dreamlike.

The great refrigerator held three gallons of cider, all in quart bottles. We drank it out of cows' horns and because the horns were small, just under half a pint, we lost count of what we drank, and so last night, I fell into a trance listening to the roar from those lights, and my father's hands fusing into every motion, casting onto the ceiling those constantly palpitating motions, shadow plays of butterflies, my eyelids heavy until my mother's voice was shouting that he should be ashamed giving me cider and her carrying me down the garden stroking the back of my head, her smell, and me getting heavier every day so that one day she would not be able to carry me to bed.

That was yesterday.

Last night.

Before my Dad went to the pub. And now I was cutting the grass with my little shears and a stag beetle was coming out of Miss Hudson's grave. And the thing had eyes, little black eyes and it was all black. A shining black as if it was just made. I had the feeling then that it was Miss Hudson coming out of the grave, that somehow her spirit had meta-morphosed into an insect. As I was kneeling there I felt the breath of my father on the back of my neck, it was a tobacco breath. He had seen what I had seen. He said, 'Touch its back, rub it, it will be scented, like a woman.'

And I did.

And it was true.

'They make scent out of them,' he said. 'Lipstick is made out of beetles. They grind them into dust. It's called cochineal.'

And I thought about Miss Russell who was my teacher and had a great heaving bosom and wore red lipstick and had huge earrings that swung when she turned her head. She who hugged me, who had kissed me after I had pinched my finger in the lid of the desk, she who had felt my tears running down her bosom that day that I had pinched my finger.

'She wouldn't put that on her face,' I said.

'Your mother does not wear lipstick,' my father replied.

'Miss Russell,' I said.

And my father said nothing because she used to play the piano when he did comic turns and came home late.

I suppose I thought that the beetle was tame or if it was in fact a reincarnation of Miss Hudson then it would know me. Instead it bit me, it hung onto my finger. I was shaking my hand a full minute after it flew off and then when I looked at my hand again I saw twin blobs of blood (the very same kind of blobs that are left when a nurse takes a sample of your blood). I shook my hand again and then I licked my finger.

At the far end of the cemetery somewhere inside the topmost branches of the Lebanon cedar a pigeon cooed. And then a breeze started to move the branches so that the sound became a humming. It was as if those sounds were trying to concentrate all my past memories of Miss Hudson.

Miss Hudson the spinster who lived during the summer months in a wooden shed at the end of our road behind the hawthorn hedge and the one single giant cedar tree with green cones, a tree that whistled in the wind. A tree that sheltered Miss Hudson, her shed house and garden. She had arches with roses and a clematis with blue flowers that climbed a crab apple tree so that in springtime there were two kinds of flowers and bumble bees swarming and my father said that it was a waste of space, that you could keep a family in taters on that land, but my mother said that he would not understand. And then one day Miss Hudson gave me a baby sumach tree.

'It comes from Canada,' she said. And I ran home with it, cupped in my hands and as I planted that tree I thought about an uncle who rode a bicycle somewhere in Alberta.

That was what my Dad had said when I told him that one of the boys in my class had an uncle who drove a tank. 'Well, you got an uncle that rides a bike in Canada,' he said.

There was no floor in Miss Hudson's shed. Just dirt. A dirt floor. She used to water it with a green watering can. A can with a giant sunflower painted on its side. There were two rooms in there. One was eight foot long and three foot wide and contained a small table with a large china jug and matching china bowl. There were forget-me-nots on the single curtained material that hid the other things beneath the table. The other room, her main room, was filled with a double bed so that there was hardly enough room to move. Miss Hudson had on her small table a photograph of a man in RAF uniform.

No one knew exactly where Miss Hudson had come from. All I could remember at that time when the beetle bit me was that my sister and I used to sit on her bed and listen to her lonely monologues about Battersea. They were days of quiet concentrated talking and while we listened, sitting among the pillows on the large bed, we saw the King taking the salute and Christopher Robin with Alice and then the room grew smaller as the shadows of the evening merged with the flickering of the oil lamp and we all three of us listened to the whispering of the wind in the trees.

It was at about the time when her health began to fail and she would spend whole days in bed surrounded by bottles of homoeopathic medicine and boxes of pills. And then the bitter sweet smell of illness settled like a rug on the dirt floor and then the wallpaper began to fall off the wall. It was as if the shed was wilting into a womb of darkness.

And then she died

My mother said it was of a broken heart.

After the sounds of me sucking my finger left my head I looked up at the cedar moving its branches like waves in the wind, the pigeon cooing and then floating in on the back of the wind the bell from the church arriving, the eight o'clock single bell tolling and my father rolling our shears into the hessian sacks and him making a seat on the front carrier out of his kneeling pad, and then him sitting on his bike, balancing, while he helped me ceremoniously up into the carrier and then he leant down on the pedals and there was a crowd of people on Ludford Bridge who turned and watched us, me with my hair streaming, my eyes running, hanging on for dear life, him pedalling so that he would gather enough speed and climb Lower Broad Street, able to arrive at the pub without stopping and breathless he helped me down and people still watching and I wasn't surprised that they were unable to tear themselves away from the sight of us arriving.

Each of the regulars at the Wheatsheaf had his own glass. There were straight and bulbous pewter pint mugs and half pint mugs, there was a straight glass engraved with Blackpool Tower, glasses with customers' initials stamped on the side and there was a left-handed glass that was used by the left-handed postman who had been drinking an hour before anyone else because he would be the first to go. He would go at nine and be up before dawn.

It amazed me what they used to discuss. Dick Williams used to talk about how he could graft roses and how he would gather up the tennis balls of manure dropped by the horse that drew the bread van or milk float.

They all laughed at that

He had the oldest rose in England, Rosa Gallica Officinalis. Father said that he spent all his time looking up Latin names in a dictionary.

They were laughing at that.

And then they had an argument about what was the difference between a French bell jar and an English one, and Mac Knight, who was a barber and stood only four foot six but was once six foot two, having shrunk on account of the fact that he had knocked at the door of a house at precisely the same moment as a land mine went off and was left there holding the door knocker. 'It was the shock shrunk me,' he said. He said that there was a nursery in Evesham that used the French ones and that they were straight-sided.

The gardener from the big house, the man who had trained fan-tailed peaches to grow all along the south-facing garden wall, agreed that they were straight-sided and he knew, since it was he who had grown garden peas that were cooked and eaten on the first race meeting in spring and that was before Easter!

Dick Williams screwed up his eyes like razor blade slits and said that Fred Reeves had said that the straight-sided bell jars were French and that Mac Knight was correct and no one wanted to argue with anything that Fred Reeves said, since he was a school boss at the Grammar School and a big noise in the allotments association. And the butcher who had his own slaughterhouse wanted to know what it mattered, but nobody liked him because he killed pigs.

Every evening this select group would show up and settle at the same table. And if I came with my father they all made a fuss and bought me a bottle of Vimto and a packet of crisps and then I was sent into the back room that was Mrs Rogers' living room and stroked the cat. But I could hear all that went on in the bar.

Them drinking and shouting about how the Americans would destroy the fishing if someone didn't stop them driving their Jeeps up and down the river with extensions on the exhaust pipe. It was a hell of a time. The Americans were let out of the camp to visit the town, blacks one day and whites the next, and there was one woman who had been seen with a white one and on another night a black one.

'OI ... OI,' they all said, and then they were laughing.

And then they started arguing about which race had the biggest willy and it was decided that it was the black mon since he came down from the trees last but that did not explain the reason why Sunshine had one the same size as anyone else's, but someone was explaining that although he was black, he had been here before the war and was just the same as us.

And then they were all laughing.

And then my Dad was telling them how when he was digging a hole in the road in Tenbury a big American truck came round the corner and the front wheel slowly dropped into the hole and how Roland Jones who had been digging the hole started to shout at the GI who was driving that he was a stupid black bastard, and how when the driver got down and said that his name was Rollin' Jones, Roland said, 'Bugger me, I never knewed I got black cousins.'

That set them off laughing again.

And then my Dad told them that when they'd got the truck out of the hole Roland said that they would have to have a drink on the strength of the fact that he'd got a black cousin.

They were laughing again.

'Did yer go with um?' someone asked.

'I did,' my Dad said, 'and let me tell you that there ain't very much wrong with them blacks, that mon could drink a pint as well as the next un.'

'Did yer see his willy?' someone asked.

And they were laughing again. It seemed that they would laugh at anything.

'It's him,' someone shouted over the laughter.

And then they stopped laughing. The door of the private room opened and two great black Somalian bodyguards came in. The Emperor Haile Selassie himself had arrived. He did not come into the private room but remained in the bar. The guards in their colourful red robes and huge swords took their places and as usual Mrs Rogers came and warmed up milk so that they each had a mug of hot cocoa.

'Poor things,' she said, 'and so far from home, you must be cold'. But the guards said nothing. It was obvious that they were well behaved and natural and I was wondering, as Mrs Rogers placed a cup of cocoa in front of me, if they had big willies like the black Americans were supposed to have.

The door between the private room and the bar was left open so that I could hear everything that was going on in the bar. They had started to play dominoes and because he was a King and an Emperor and he was the Lion of Judea (that is what my mother said he was when she had pointed him out to me when we were up town last Monday), because he was all those things, he made more noise than the others. He would bang his dominoes down on the table and then so as to make him feel at home the others played in the same way, banging the table each time they had to knock. And then they were explaining that it was no good him putting half a crown down, that he had to have a penny since it was a penny a knock and so they spent some time explaining how many pennies there were in half a crown and then the Emperor had a great pile of coins but the pile got smaller the more he played because my Dad was a good domino player and had as many silver cups as the King had crowns. But the Emperor, the King, held his own.

I never knew he had that double six.

I thought that blank five was sleeping.

It's you ta shuffle.

Meanwhile Mrs Rogers brought in a plate of home made biscuits and the guards dipped the biscuits in their cocoa and then I did the same and the guards became relaxed because everything was under control. And I thought about it all, and was happy that I lived in the town where I lived because after all this town was such an important town, a town where once the parliament of England had sat and so it was a natural thing that we would have a King sitting in playing dominoes with my father. It was just very sad that the poor King had lost all his lands.

I was bored and without knowing how it happened I stood up and went into the bar and stood next to the Emperor and him so small in his chair, dressed in a grey uniform with a peaked cap on his head placed his hand on my head and it was as if the Rev Carver was blessing me because his hand was warm.

And then I felt that everyone was watching me so I went back into the private room to where the guards were dunking their biscuits and I too dunked mine and then I felt myself falling off the chair and into the arms of one of the great black guards and he smelt, he smelt just like my grandfather did when he came home from working in the bakery, a sweating smell that comforted me.

The next thing that I remembered was being tied onto the carrier of my father's bike with a red scarf and the free wheel ticking and the dynamo humming as we went downhill towards home. And the wind, tears forming in my eyes, hissing in my ears so that if I turned my head it was silent in one ear and me still holding the steel carrier because it was dark beside the river and the air beside the garage thick with petrol and I could feel heavy rain drops falling in isolation and the downpour of the black river falling over the horseshoe weir, and my father breathing as he pedalled, nothing but those sounds, floating in the night sky.

And then we were at the gasworks, riding across the blue-black sets to the sliding door that was half drawn like a giant curtain so that I could see the retort and the stoker naked to the waist shovelling coal into the mouth, his fire-illuminated body sweating, dancing gracefully at the purity of his task and all the time that great fire sucking so much oxygen that there was a draught around us, and the fat yellow light dimming as the stoker smothered those hungry blue-green flames and then as the last shovelful was gathered into the last heap, the stoker leaned on his shovel and putting his right hand on the bridge of his nose he blew twin streams of snot onto that heap and then he shot the last shovelful, his snot and all right into the fire, and then the draught disappeared as he shut the iron door and sealed it with a horizontal screw.

'Have a Woodbine,' my father said, still balancing his bike with me on the carrier. And the stoker pushed his flat cap up so that the pure whiteness of his forehead looked strange above the blackness of his sweating face. And then he bent his face towards the cupped hands of my father and sucked the match firing up the cigarette.

They smoked, blue smoke rolling from their nostrils like dragons, my father and the stoker, both of them illuminated by sharp shafts of light, and then the stoker gave my father his pole with the brass hook on the end and my father put weight on the pedals of the bike and we were moving across the blue-black sets, the tender light of the lamp on the very front of the carrier becoming stronger as he pedalled faster, holding his pole like a knight's lance charging into the darkness until we slowed at the bottom of Weeping Cross Lane beneath the first pool of yellow light.

'Soon we won't do this,' my Dad said, 'when the electricity comes we won't have to do it.'

And I looked up with my father at the cluster of mantels inside the round glass globe which cast deep shadows and I listened to that melodic white hissing and I looked at the great round shade that cut off the light so that there was a distinctive area of light and shadow.

'Soon we will have modern electric street lights,' my Dad said.

And then still balancing the bike my father hooked the ring on the long chain and extinguished the light to reveal a clear pin cushion sky.

'Do you know what?' Dad said, his voice coming from deep darkness. 'It's cowed enough fer a frost.'

# 6  *Syphons*

On the wall of my bedroom my father had when I was three painted a great locomotive. It should have been a train but he painted the locomotive so big that there was only enough room left for it to pull a guard's van. There were hills, and a small shed in the valley between the hills. The shed was my father's shed, the guard in the guard's van was Mr Timmis. He was waving at Dad who stood in front of his shed holding a glass of cider. The sun shining through the window of my bedroom cast the silhouette of the window frame onto the locomotive on the wall so that it was framed in the shadow of the window frame. If I lay and watched the shadow it would move across the wall. This shadow journey took time ... it was a cosmic awareness of the rising sun. Me flat on my back still heavy with sleep, lifted up by my breathing, dreaming that my father was pouring Fred Timmis umpteen glasses of cider. That bright sun and the sound of pouring and me listening to the quiet whispering of my Mum and Dad arguing about my aunt Rhoda.

'It's a downward path,' Dad said.

'She has a right to do what she thinks fit and anyway it's her life,' Mum said.

'Downhill,' and Dad was stirring his tea.

He would be drinking from his vast pint cup, and she would not be cutting the bread for his sandwiches, not this morning. It was Saturday, and the announcer on the wireless was giving the shipping forecast. My mother always listened to the shipping forecast. I never understood how on earth Dogger Bank, Cromarty lighthouse or Finisterre could have any influence on our weather, but she would always tell Dad to shut up so that she could listen and then after he'd gone out she would listen to the normal weather forecast, all those voices mingling and then the wireless made repeated short fragments of sounds as she searched the air waves for her beloved Third Programme. I always wanted to know where the sounds that were in between the programmes came from. Mother said that they were sunspots exploding; Dad said that it was God farting.

Dad low-brow, Mum high-brow. Mum with her violin, Dad with his piano and aunt Rhoda with her violin. Aunt Rhoda was not my mother's sister but her best friend. She was a Land Girl who dressed like a man, who looked like a man who used to come down to our house for a bath every Friday evening, who had big bosoms, who looked like a violin from behind, so feminine when I saw her get out of our bath. She covered her big brown nipples when she saw me looking at her and she laughed and then she turned with her back to me and I saw her towel absorb little rivers of soap that were running down her back. Her shape when out of her trousers reminded me of a large violin.

'A weekday man, a weekend woman,' Dicky said she was.

And I knew that Dicky liked her because he waited for her on Friday nights.

Johann Christian, Johann Sebastian, Ludwig, Amadeus, aunt Rhoda and mother used the Christian names so that my father never knew where he was when they talked about music. 'The four wigged Germans' he called them …

And then the sun had moved the shadow of the frame so that it was narrow and elongated and I had faded away lying there wanting to wee with my finger and thumb holding the end of my willy because I was afraid to wet the bed … but I had to go and so I slid from the warm sheets, kneeling, the pot between my knees.

My father had left before me. That did not matter, he'd be in the stores talking about blackfly on the beans or the price of cigarettes. It never ceased to amaze me what Dad and the others at the gasworks used to find to talk about and they would all be smoking so that the stores always had a cloud of smoke hanging just above the ceiling. What with the smell of boss white and old gas fittings and stale farts, it was a wonder that the place never exploded. They would all always be laughing about something before they set out on their jobs on Saturday morning.

Saturday mornings were the best. They were not in so much of a hurry to move, it was the only morning when they drank tea.

It was syphon pumping morning. Every other Saturday Dad and I pumped the syphons so I knew that I could eat my porridge and Dad would still be there, he would be waiting for me, drinking his tea.

*A NOTE CONCERNING SYPHONS*

The first syphon was situated down the bottom of Lady Bushby's drive. Syphons are always placed at the lowest point of the gas main, at the bottom of a hill just before it rises up again, that's where the water collects. It's the water caused by condensation that gathers at this lowest point. Coal gas being damp by nature, unlike today's natural gas, carried a tremendous amount of water with it. When it collected in those difficult places, it caused the pressure to decrease. The user of the appliance, whether it were a cooker or a fire, had then of necessity to turn it up so that in extreme cases just to have the thing on low, if there was water in the pipe, it had to be turned to high. Even then there was sometimes little heat, an inconvenience when cooking meat, which would take twice as long.

The cooks relied on my father to keep the syphons clear, to keep the pressure up. He did this by lifting the lid of a small inspection cover. Then he undid a square nut that was directly on the gas main. If the pipe was full of water then there would be no escape of gas and Dad would screw on the stirrup pump and pump out the trapped water. Sometimes there would be a couple of buckets full. He could tell when it was empty, raw gas would blow out. Of course, the thing to do was to make sure that the customer knew that you were pumping the syphon. That you were looking after them.

In those days the cooks were the bosses of the great houses. Their life was made easy by the amount of gas running through their pipes. They needed good pressure. Therefore there was always a cup of tea waiting after the syphon had been pumped and since the cook at Lady Bushby's house made the finest shortbread, then there was always a small triangle on the saucer. The other thing to remember was that the money to build the gasworks had been subscribed by the rich and well-to-do. These families all lived in the large country houses with long thin sometimes private gas mains, in fact the pipes were too small. They had been there since Victorian times and were corroded on the inside so they always needed pumping. Every other Saturday my Dad made sure that they were clear.

It was almost a theatrical performance. I had to drop the bucket once or twice, depending whether or not the cook came round the back of the house to see what was happening.

Ah, it's Jack, she would shout. I wondered what was happening.

Ah, Mrs ... whatever her name was, Dad would say.

How's the pressure in yer pipes.

You're a one.

and she would wobble because she was well fed.

I'll tell you what.

What.

You wait until I get my pump coupled up to your pipe.

Oh Jack you are a one.

and she'd wobble all over the place.

I'll have um clean as a whistle in a wink.

OOOOOOOHHHHHH.

They'll be so much pressure in your range you'll boil a kettle in no time.

I'll tell you what you'll bake a bun in your oven in short order.

You are a right one.

and she would wobble and laugh.

You'll have a cup of tea Jack.

Don't mind if I do.

And the boy.

and she would come across and grab my cheek.

He does look like his father.

Her hands were cold and soft, cook's hands, and she would wobble like a jelly.

And then I had to nod and say thank you very much, although I never liked tea, or any other hot drink, come to that. But I had to have it.

'It'll break the habit if yer don't,' Dad said.

But I liked shortcakes, a good cook always made good shortcakes, so I used dunk the shortcakes in the tea, drink a few sips and pour the rest away where no one would see.

*END OF NOTE CONCERNING SYPHONS*

Along the landing pad of the manager's pigeon loft the birds were waddling, cooing and bowing at the manager who was cooing back while at the same time shovelling pigeon shit into a wooden wheelbarrow.

'Yer Dad's in there,' he shouted at me, pointing to the store room.

The store room was a long wooden building painted green so that from the air it would look like a field. It was the same shade of green as the gas holder but the gas holder had other brown patterns that looked like clouds. 'Camouflaging,' it was called.

During the war the manager wanted the gate left open between the Jockey Field and the gas holder so that Dollar Howard's donkey could walk around the gas holder. He even got Dollar Howard to build a haystack in the yard. He told the workers that the whole gasworks would look like a farmyard from the air, but my father and I had climbed to the top of the church steeple with Cocky Wontner. Right up beside the lightning conductor we climbed, and we'd looked over the edge at the whole town and we saw the painted gasworks, Clee Hill and all the woodlands and the river which flowed around the town and we saw that our town was on a hill and in a valley and had two bridges and because of that it was a natural fortified town.

Cocky noted the fact and said it didn't matter a tinker's cuss any more: 'A fortified town is now redundant. If Jerry wanted to, he could bomb the whole town, but they wouldn't do it on account of the fact that our town ain't worth anything any more. They don't bomb market towns. We got no factories, we don't make anything except cows. Jerry dunna care a toss about us, that's why it's a good place to live. We could be in Coventry, then we'd be right in the shit.'

We thought about that and Dad observed that people in the streets were walking about like ants and Cocky shouted:

'LUCKY BASTARDS,' as loud as he could but no one looked up.

That upset Cocky and he said that he had something that would make them look up and he pulled from his pocket a brassiere that he'd got from somewhere and ran it up the flag pole and then people looked up and so we ran down the spiral stairs leaving the new flag flying and all the running round and round made me giddy and sick so much so that I vomited in the Rose and Crown yard, which pleased Cocky so much that he told the landlord that I had travel sickness and had just come off the bus from Knighton and he bought me a packet of crisps.

'We now know, Jack,' he said, wiping his mouth after the first deep swallow of beer, 'that anyone who believes Jerry would mistake a gasworks fer a farmyard is an idiot.'

Now the war was over and Cocky was right. The Germans only dropped one bomb on our town and that was an accident. It landed just behind the church and they charged threepence to look at the hole. That was a long time ago. The hole has only just been filled in. It takes a long time to do things in our town, which is why the gasworks is still painted in its wartime livery.

'Start the siren, that'll shift them,' the manager shouted as he pushed his wheelbarrow of pigeon shit towards the midden.

I liked him when he told me to do that. The siren had a long handle and was very hard to turn but once you got it moving, it gathered speed so that by the time your arm was a blur the thing was screaming, an unpleasant noise that hung over the gasworks like dense mushrooms forcing the men out of the stores and then when they saw me they would shout at me, mouthing obscenities. They looked like actors in a silent film, waving their arms at me because of the siren's din.

'You're gettin' too big fer this lark,' Dad said as I climbed into the carrier.

I was.

As we approached Ludford Bridge, the bridge that the great Thomas Telford rebuilt, my Dad pulled in to the kerb and waited for me to slide out of the carrier before he dismounted and then he lifted his bike onto the path. There was an RAF transporter loaded with a wing from a Spitfire turning onto the bridge. It was a tight squeeze. The Scammell transporter was roaring in first gear, closely observed by two men and a dog. The dog was running along the parapet of the bridge. One of the men was Boneyard Johnson (it was his dog), the other was Paddy Reynolds.

We all watched the unit move across the bridge, taking the noise of its engine with it. As the silence returned I saw the yellow sunlight drench the surface of the river and swarms of midges dancing just above the flow from the central arch.

'There's a pike down there,' Boneyard said, pointing to where the current slowed as it backed up behind the weir.

'He's never been here before,' Paddy said, looking at where the transporter had gone.

'Who?' Dad said.

'The driver,' Paddy said, swinging back round to face us, his eyes slightly rounded. 'Gloucester, that's where he's going.'

'Shobdon,' Boneyard said.

'Bomber airport, that is,' Paddy said.

'What der you know about it?' Boneyard said as he turned to Dad. 'This here prat thinks that his hair's turned white because a parachute never opened at a thousand feet.'

'It did, too,' and Paddy lifted his peaked cap and a great mop of silver hair fell out and over his face so that he had to brush it out of his eyes.

'Jack,' he shouted, 'Jack knows,' and he was pointing at Dad.

'The highest he's ever been is the castle tower,' said Boneyard.

'I was up the North Pole,' shouted Paddy, who was getting more than a little heated.

'My arse,' shouted Boneyard.

'It was so cold up there that the fire froze,' said Paddy.

'Oh blessed Ada, he's off again,' and Boneyard stroked his dog, who licked his face.

'Yes, and the flame froze and it was so cold that I had to run up and get that flame down and thaw it out on a brazier and then run up again when it was lit so that the planes wouldn't hit the pole at night, it was a hell of a thing,' and then Paddy flopped his head backwards and gathered his silver hair back under his cap so that he looked as if he had no hair.

'There's a pike down there,' Boneyard said, 'and I'm going to have that bastard, ain't I, Toby?' and the dog licked his face again.

A two-door Austin Seven moved onto the bridge. It was followed by 'Jigger' the great black stallion galloping with Jack Magrath's daughter Jane on its back. They both galloped as if they were one, Miss Magrath opening her legs slightly as she moved the stallion towards the centre of the road.

'Shavings,' Boneyard said, and his dog barked.

'Sooty Prats,' Dad said.

'Ah, that's where her's goin,' Paddy said. 'Her's got an account there.'

Suddenly there was a flash of lightning way down the river and then the sound of an explosion from the same direction.

'The bastards,' Boneyard shouted.

'Them bloody Americans,' said Paddy.

'Fishin' uth hand grenades,' said Boneyard, 'I've sin it all now, fuckin' Yanks, Better off uth the Jerries than them bastards.'

'They won the war fer us,' Paddy said.

'My arse,' said Boneyard

'Good job as her weren't on the bridge,' said Dad.

And then just as my Dad spoke there was another explosion and a white cloud and then the black stallion started to prance outside the garage and you could see even in the morning's bright light sparks kindled like flints and puffs of breath rolling from the beast's nostrils and his eyes were crazed with fear as he reared up and kicked the red watering can with Fire in black letters on its side across the road and the girl leaning forward as he pranced, all the buckles and straps under that shining saddle straining, her riding breeches stretching, up on his rear hooves, sparks flying and Charlie Wotten the petrol pump attendant all stiff with fear and if he had not jumped out of the way he would have been trampled to death as that horse bolted and then the hooves grew silent in the soft mud that had been churned up by the trucks that stopped overnight on the open land and her ginger hair flying in the wind betraying her Irish ancestry as she fought that great stallion who was certainly not neutered, her hair and his blowing mane streaming until him standing still, trembling, her stroking and patting his neck, and she was stroking him with her hand but not the whip she was holding.

'Good God,' said Paddy with his eyes all standing out and round.

And then no one said a word. For a full minute there was silence. Even the river seemed to move quietly over the rocks.

'That's better than the pictures,' said Paddy.

'Her con use that whip on me any time her likes,' Boneyard said scratching his backside.

'More chance of fryin' a snowball than that,' said Dad and he was laughing.

'What an arse,' Paddy said.

'Good God,' said Boneyard, looking at Paddy. 'You're dangerous, you are. Thought that you lost all that when you fell out'a the plane.'

'I got more than you thinks, an I got a pension to boot,' Paddy said.

And then there was another silence.

'It's the horse ridin,' said Boneyard. 'Creates a perfect arse, does a horse. Them toffs knows a thing or two about omen and horses. A perfect arse … Ah, makes um tight, all tight, all right.'

And then I saw that Dad was laughing and shaking his head.

And we left the bridge after Miss Magrath had calmed her bolting horse. Me on Dad's bike, hanging on in the wind, because we were moving through the air and all the time me thinking about what was so interesting about a tight arse so that when we came to Mile End, to the stone Roman mile post that was one mile out of town, where the next syphon was, I'd almost forgot where it was, until the free wheel was ticking away and we were at walking pace looking for the steel cover that was overgrown and then I jumped down holding Dad's bike upright, which was easy if you held it bolt upright, but heavy if you let it fall to one side.

He had a way of moving the nettles, my Dad. He used to kick backwards with his right leg in a circular motion, the heel of his boot cutting like a blade so that you could see all the nails in his boot.

'Why do horses make perfect arses?' I asked my Dad in extreme simplicity.

'It's the saddle,' he said. 'It's a hell of a powerful thing, is a saddle, them being right up there looking down.'

And then he stopped cutting back the grass, having found the little steel hinged trap door and he paused before doing a perfect pirouette and said,

'Nothing is as expensive as a woman's arse.'

'Even a train set?' I said.

'Nothing is as expensive as a woman's arse ... now, give us that pump.'

And I looked at Dad and I saw in his eyes that he knew something that I did not know ... yet.

And because we were in the middle of the country and outside Mile End House and right next to a drain, my father pumped the water into the ditch and it smelt like the gasworks smelt.

And then Dad was pedalling hard as we passed a

field of white-brown coloured cows that I knew were Herefords because Cocky Wontner had told me all about the herds that he had seen on his last visit to America and how he had driven one thousand head across the Rocky Mountains.

'The high saddle is a power for the gentry,' said Dad.

And the cows watched us moving the other side of the hedge and their expressions changed slowly, giving us to understand that they knew where we were going, them swinging long tails across their backs or sitting chewing and I waved to them as a sign of my appreciation.

'It was the centaurs
half man and half horse,'
Dad spoke between deep breaths
'They came down out of the steppes of central Russia
hell of a thing
'to them poor buggers as saw it first
of course there was no such thing
but it was the first time that the Greeks saw them
men sitting up on the back of a horse
and swinging a great sword
looked like as if they were joined as one
half man and half horse
to them defeated souls who ran like hell
not many escaping
and so the myth was born
a hell of a powerful thing is a saddle
that not so much as shapes the bottom
but gives it a cultivated look
as it were
and women not havin' the same tackle as we
used to ride side-saddle
on account of their

bustles and skirts
which got in the way
and them all ladylike and not movin' their legs
with ease
like a mon
they used to slide down both legs together
almost ashamed of their legs they were ...
Huh huh huh huh ... that's enough.'
Dad was out of breath.

The bike slowed down on the hill and Dad lifted his leg over the saddle and we stopped, me sliding down to the ground and him leaning on his saddle, his face a masterpiece of mirth, his eyes and lips all rounded.

'And ladies' bikes don't have a cross bar,' he said.

'Why?' I asked.

'They got different tackle,' he said.

And I could not quite understand how that would make any difference and anyway it was more difficult to cock your leg over having balls than for my sister who had nothing down there to get in the way like the girl next door who had let me look at her while she counted to one hundred, a sight not worth the price of the great Jack marble that I gave her for the privilege. 'Don't touch,' she said, looking at me as she bent down, me looking at her bum hole which was surprisingly smaller than the other part and so I left off looking when she got to fifty because there was nothing to get excited about anyway.

'The best saddles are leather,' said Dad, 'uth springs, gives you more of a bounce, extremely easy on your bollocks.'

And then we started to walk up the long hill towards the gatehouse where an old man was brushing the drive beneath the giant wrought iron gate.

A small figure labouring away taking his time so that he would still be there when we arrived.

The flowers in the small garden of the gatehouse just grew as they would if left to themselves. It was as if the flowers were no one's business, they just grew perfect in their own imperfection. There was no soil to be seen, just the strong simple lines of the cottage softened by the mass of spring flowers.

The old man squinted his milk blue eyes against the glare of the sun, grinned and pushed his flat cap back over his head revealing a white-skinned forehead.

'Er wants ta see you,' he said, laughing as he spoke. 'There ain't enough pressure in her stove ta boil an egg.'

'I'll pump er syphon right out just now, Mr Wilson,' Dad said.

And then I saw an old spaniel begin to materialise slowly out of the murk beyond the door and when the dog reached the threshold it started snuffling and its ears were flapping and its feet padded along the path between the flowers. The animal smelt of dog, he came up and sniffed at the old man's trousers. The old man rubbed the dog's neck.

'You old dog,' Mr Wilson said, pushing the dog away with his foot, but the dog wanted more and so Mr Wilson rubbed, saying, 'This ere dog's older than me. Twenty years, that's seven to our one, makes im one hundred and forty years old. And when he goes I won't have another un, an I'm ninety four, so he's waitin' fer me to go, and I'm waitin' fer im to go, but we ain't gonna go like that.'

And as the man rubbed the dog you could feel the smell rising from it.

'I knowed that you was comin' because me gas lifted like a flamin' blow torch under the kettle.'

'I got a gallon and a half out of Mile End,' Dad said. 'About ten minutes ago.'

'That uld be it,' Mr Wilson replied, 'made the water rattle like ball bearings, it did.I knowed that you was comin' when I heard the kettle rattle. Der want a cup of tea?'

'Na,' Dad replied. 'We just ad one.'

And I was glad because the house was murky and dark and there was newspaper on the table and the tea would be strong like my Grandad's tea and there would be no tea strainer.

'Here, do yer know about the paintin' in the hall?' Mr Wilson asked.

'What one?' Dad said.

'The bull terrier,' the old man said, 'Staffordshire bull terrier.'

The sun was high in the sky, the morning was awash in a sea of golden beams because of the dust from a faint wisp of wind, and the old man's garden was silent, just the dog panting, and next to the gate a thrush singing. When the thrush stopped there was a silence, the old man waiting for the prompt from Dad, a nod the right to continue.

'So,' started the old man, scratching his head, 'as you goes in through the door on the right next to where the pantry is, you'um in the kitchen now, where the cook works in the big room where her does the preparing and then there is the lobby where all the bells are, next to that in the corridor, that's where the painting is. The Staffordshire bull terrier uth the jaws. Well, it was in my great grand-father's time and that was when there used to be journeymen artists that used to come round and live in fer a couple of months. They had board and keep, like, but they was no better than any other journeymen come to that, exceptin' that they could paint a portrait in oils. All the canvasses and the big easel they had and what they done was to do the paintin' and then before it was half finished, like, then they would look round for some other big house who needed a paintin' doin'. And they was always in work since there was marryin' and some reachin' the age of twenty-one or army officers, they always had work anyroad. This un took to one of the scullery maids, and old Roger de Lacy always thought that he was takin' too long and told him so. Well, at the final sitting at that time when payment was due old Roger don't pay him enough and the artist got wild and all worked up so he tells Roger that he wants another week. Well, that give him access to the maid and food, like. And that's all a mon wants in life is a full drum and an empty dick.'

The old man sighed and a wise grin started to spread in the folds of his face.

'Well now,' he said, 'that's how it was and Old Roger being not such a bad old stick never held it against him even though the artist took the scullery maid away and he left the picture hangin' on the wall where it still is today, scowling down atcha. And it was a funny thing you know, old Roger grew more and more like that dog and it is said that if you pass the black pond at midnight you'll be more than likely to see a great bull terrier jump out at yer. Ron Wall saw it one night, drunk with cider he was … sober when he got home. But I heared that dog many a time.'

'What did it sound like,' I asked, 'a wolf ?'

'Nope.'

'What did it sound like?' I asked again.

And Mr Wilson looked at me. He had a benign look on his face and his head began to shake.

'Well, I'll tell yer,' he said. 'It is like a mad dog howlin' back into eternity.'

And then I saw that Dad was fixing to leave and so I went round to the carrier and my seat and Dad lifted me up.

'You're gettin' too big fer this,' he said.

'I know,' I said.

'Well, we'll have ta do summat about it then,' he said as he pushed down on the pedal while at the same time waving goodbye to Mr Wilson who was still scratching the old dog's ear. 'But first we'll take a look at uld Roger's picture.'

And we both waved to Mr Wilson and his old dog.

And I felt happy thinking that perhaps Dad was going to get me a bike.

# 7   *Nihil Sine Labore*

Our road climbed slowly to the beginning of the
hamlet that marks the start of Sunny Gutter. As we
came over the top and round the corner we could
see the first of the topiary trees, a handsome box
spiral. This tree is framed by an arch of old English
dog roses all exuberant and pink. Next to it a
thatched cottage surrounded by a close clipped
box hedge. This is the home of Ronnie Small the
barber ... Ronnie one ball, the barber with only
one ball. And as we move along the side of his
house more topiary, a giant peacock on a plinth
with an unclipped tail in full display and the brown
thatch above the yellow stone walled cottage curved
from our distance, looking like the camouflage on
the gasworks gas holder.

How does anyone get a tree to grow into a spiral?
Is it cruel, how does he do it. I suppose that it must
be similar to cutting hair, cutting box trees. But it
takes years to achieve the shape, I know that
because Dad tried to do it with the old yew tree. He
tried to make it into a square box, he tried to cut it
into a box but he spoilt it. It was not a box it was
out of shape and so he decided that it would be a
triangle but the centre trunk was in the way and so
he was left with a hacked away tree and then when

Mr Poole asked him what on earth he was doing to the tree, Dad said:

'I'm cutting it down, what do yer think I'm doing with it'.

'It was a good tree', said Harry Poole, 'took a hundred years to grow that big'.

'Damn thing was wrapping its roots around the sewer pipe', said Dad.

And Dad was all red faced and he had beads of sweat dropping from his forehead. And then Mr Poole looked as if he knew more about what was around our house than Dad did.

'You got sewer pipes front and back?' he asked.

'All around our house we got um', Dad said. And as if to rub it in he said, 'we got storm drains as well'.

And then after a very long pause Mr Poole said, 'You'll need to remove the stump then.'

'I'm going to remove every single bit of the f ... ing tree'

And Dad said the f-word to Mr Poole and I saw that it was a very powerful word because Mr Poole started to walk away and would probably have to write it on a piece of paper because he would not be able to tell Mrs Poole directly, since she was very big in the church and then Dad said that he would like to remove Mr Poole from off the face of the Earth.

At the end of that day all that there was left was a hole that looked like as if a giant tooth had been extracted and a great heap of branches that burnt in the biggest fire that we have ever had at our house so it was worth it just for the fire.

'I suppose it must be similar to cutting hair, cutting box trees', Mum said over supper.

'AAhh,' Dad said, 'you gotta ave a special brain to do it.'

I thought what Dad said about brains and Ronnie Small's single ball and was glad that I had two.

Perhaps that's why Ronnie Small cuts the trees the way he does and I wondered about it as we descended that day towards Roger de Lacy's. I wondered if that was why Spud Taylor had to go into hospital to have his other ball lowered so that he would not grow into a barber and be obsessed with cutting things.

I know that Roger de Lacy's house is Tudor, that it was given to his family after the civil war and that Roger de Lacy's family were friends of the Duke of York and that they spelt friend, frend, and that they, those people from that time spelt things the way they sounded and that I was having trouble at my small inkwell desk. Trouble with the words and the way they were spelt. I had found out about 'phonetic spelling' and whilst all the others in my class just went ahead and learnt I just sat there thinking about the Tudors and how smart they were spelling words the way they sounded.

It was something that I could not just overcome. And then Mrs Lloyd my teacher told my Mother that I was not trying, but I was trying, I was trying to understand and then Mrs Lloyd made me write every word that I could not spell one hundred times so that I called the 'Friars walk', (an alley on our way to school) 'Agony Way'. I dreamt that I was Gandhi sitting in that alley, that every one was looking at me, even the tiles on the roofs fell onto me. But I never moved. I decided to stop learning.

I had great respect for the Tudors. I liked Roger de Lacy's great stone yellow-honey-coloured building with stone balustrades where you would normally expect to see the guttering. And the slate roof rising up and the ends capped in ornate stone coping stones. I could never understand how the water ran off the gutterless roof. I always wanted to be there when it rained a real storm, like the one last month when the rain came down so hard that it was as if there was just solid water out there outside our house, water that you might drown in if you did go outside. It was no wonder the way it rained that day. The drains became so full that they could take no more, and the sewer was so full that the great man-hole cover in the centre of the road lifted up and we waited for a car to come down the road so that it would fall into the manhole, but none came.

There were only two car owners down our street, Mr Pilkington and the manager of the Birmingham water works, Mr Wilmot, and they would not have gone out in such a storm and anyway if they had done, then my Dad would have rushed out to wave them down.

That manhole cover remained open until Mr Shenton came down on his bike and swept the beached turds back before replacing the lid and then he came round to inspect Dad's tobacco plants that had some kind of mildew on them. A disease that could only be cured in the shed whilst drinking cider that had just been delivered the day before. Both Mr Shenton and my father wondering how the storm had affected the drink in the barrel.

'I don't think that it has done it any harm,' Mr Shenton said after the third glass.

And then he fell off his bike due to the mud that had been left on the road ... I wondered how Roger de Lacy's gutter in his great house had stood up to that storm.

'Nihil sine labore', so proclaims the Gothic-lettered

inscription over the doorway to those tradesmen using the tradesman's entrance, and Dad always said as he passed that sign that Roger had never done a day's work in his life.

'Made his fortune out of the sugar trade', Dad said, 'out of slavery', he said, but they were once the main shareholders in the gas works, that was why they had gas so far out of town, that was why they had to have the syphon pumped every month. I marvelled at the power of the Aristocracy, those who were so powerful that even though now that the gas works was nationalised Dad still pumped their syphons.

Dad always announced his presence to Muriel the cook who would always be in the kitchen. The kitchen was at the end of a dark passage, all the light came in through four leaded windows the bottoms of which were at head height and impossible to see out of. This was because the kitchen was below ground level and therefore always at the same temperature, cool. As we entered the kitchen it felt as if the whole world was closing in on us. I felt unable to breathe. Every time I went into that house I felt that I shrank, always the same impression that behind those great high windows were pairs of eyes watching. It must have been the oak panelled walls of the corridor, dark oak walls covering something, leading into a dark cool kitchen.

There was a dance band on the wireless, playing an old hymn. It was almost silent, distantly strident, a shimmering somnolence over the top of the vapour of fumes floating over the great double-ovened coke-fired stove that was next to a gas cooker with the legend 'Cannon' on its door.

Dad called her Muriel. Out loud he shouted her name. We knew that she was there when the room's light dropped a couple of octaves. She was a big woman.

'Jack,' she said.

And she looked at me as she said the word, before she looked at Dad who was all the time looking at her standing in the door until she moved around the refectory table with her head scarf knotted on top of her head and her long sleeved rolled up, green and yellow cardigan, her and my Dad looking at each other like sometimes Mum and Dad looked at each other and I knew that her husband was in the army somewhere in Burma which was a place worse than Germany because of the jungle which was tropical whereas Germany had a climate like ours ... and then from the wireless Major Glenn Miller shouted 'Jeep Jockey Jump' and Dad turned up the sound and as the music filled the great kitchen it started to paint a moving picture so that both of them speeded up as they approached each other as if they were filling a great gap and suddenly Dad was all handsome as Muriel took him by his hands and they danced a kind of childish dance him, my father swinging his head so hard that his cap flew off his head and her lifting her hand above her head so that she pulled the knot on her head scarf and she threw it away, her hair set in a roll at the nape of her neck so that I saw her ears and her eyes were full of tears. And he took her in his arms and they danced until Jeep Jockey Jump had finished and then he wiped his brow and she combed his hair with her fingers. And he sat down and breathed out. A man of such nobility, she said. And then the middle bell on the end of a curled spring started to move before it rang, a signal ... sending everything into the opposite direction dissolving the visions of carnality and sentimentality into a dirty melted slush.

'He wants his elevenses,' she said.

And so we both went out the same way that we had come and the little iron trap was in amongst the gravel path where it had been since the gas was installed and Dad took a long screwdriver from his tool bag and lifted the lid and I saw that his hands were ingrained with dirt and the nails on those hands were all cracked and there was just the sound of the stirrup pump sucking, a breathing until it vomited up a brown liquid that smelt of tar.

Three bucketfuls came up that pipe, two bucketfuls I carried to a midden that was surrounded in stinging nettles and then I saw the peacock perched on the stone balustrade looking at us snake like. And I looked back at that peacock until the bird moved towards me in ever decreasing semi circles.

And then Dad said, 'Here. I might as well do it myself.'

And then he snatched the final bucket carrying it to the midden which meant that I should not have been there in the kitchen and seen that dance.

Determined to see for myself the painting of the dog, that my Dad had seemed to have forgotten about, when Muriel called Dad for a cup of tea, I went ahead leaving them both in the kitchen and following my nose I found myself in the parlour and drawn curtains so that the upholstered chairs were like shadows and the tapestry of a knight on horseback looked dull compared to the painting of the train on the wall of my bedroom.

There was a monumental stone staircase leading to the first floor and the great chamber. The great chamber was a library containing an ornate plasterwork ceiling and frieze and a spectacular Portland stone chimney piece flanked by Corinthian columns. The windows were set with brightly coloured heraldic stained-glass windows that traced the genealogy of the De Lacy family. The first painting was of young Edward, a master builder with his mother Elizabeth. She was a long nosed woman dressed in a long satin low cut dress sitting in a giant red upholstered chair that looked like a throne. Edward was standing next to her and was wearing a blue coat with brass buttons unbuttoned, open. He had red lips and a powdered face with a blond wig that made him look anaemic. His mother's face was the same complexion as her son's. But her nose was long and pinkish and the thing about them was that they had beautiful hands. Long and slender hands that had never done any work.

She was not as attractive as Muriel who had danced with my father except that she had those long hands. And then there was a dark painting of someone who looked like a monk. He held a quill pen and was about to write but there was no paper.

Then I saw it. There it was, the dog's face on a man's body. At first it looked like a cartoon that was on the wall of the antiques shop in Broad Street that sold framed prints. The dog's face was almost human and the artist had had to paint saliva foaming at its jaws to make it look vicious and next to it a portrait of Walter Raleigh or someone like him and there seemed to be all the Kings and Queens of England looking disdainful, down at me in that room.

And yet it felt so safe and then I knew why it was that the Germans had lost the war. It would take more than a war to remove what was in the confines of this house. All the gold-tooled leather bound books in the oak shelves each side of the fireplace. A fireplace with a chimney-piece so finely executed in carved marble that although the curtains in the room were drawn it shone like a brown mirror.

There were two handles each side of the fireplace curved like an 'S', china handles, so that who ever wanted to could summon his or her wants from the kitchen. I wondered whether Dad was dancing down there with Muriel, who was once my mother's best friend but had married a soldier from Shrewsbury. I felt myself moving my hands towards those handles when all of a sudden the room became flooded in a dense dazzling light and as I turned an old man stood there looking at me.

He was wearing a green cape that was still swinging around his tall thin body. He was stationary standing there looking at me. Me who was not supposed to be in his room.

'Sir', I said. and he pulled from his pocket a brass trumpet that he placed in his ear so that for a moment it looked like as if it was his ear, him edging towards me, sideways, 'Sir,' I said again, this time into the trumpet and then he said,

'Boy, you must be the gas man's brat.'

And because I was I nodded but he wanted me to speak into his trumpet and so I said once again 'Sir' as his head came round so that the trumpet was facing me.

'Pull it boy, pull it towards the grate', he said and I looked at him pointing at the handles and I pulled it and it must have been on some kind of spring because it went back to where it was before but there was no indication whatever that it had rung so I pulled it again. And I pulled it again for my Mother who was once Muriel's best friend and was down there with my Dad.

'Enough', he said smiling and he walked with great dignity towards me and lifting his hand that held the miniature trumpet he laid it upon my shoulder and both of us together looked at the paintings and when I looked more closely at the dog's face I began to read the meaning behind the facial expression of the dog and it seemed to me that the expressions were constantly changing so that I was reading the character of the man behind the dog and I realised that what I saw was imposed on the face of a man who looked like the man who was holding the quill pen. And so I looked up at Roger de Lacy who had his hand on my shoulder and saw his nose which was almost pointed like the man holding the quill pen.

'My grandfather,' Roger said. 'Do you know the legend?'

And every time he wanted a response he swung his head round and placed the trumpet to his ear and held it there until I shouted,

'Yes, sir.'

Roger de Lacy walked with great dignity and unction in front of his paintings and then he pointed towards the shelves holding the books.

'There is no finer university than a library of books,' he shouted because he was deaf.

And then there was a profound silence and stillness in the room and the plaster frieze that ran high along the top of the wall seemed to be holding up the whole world.

I stood there in that room amongst all that magnificence facing it with admiration and awe, praying that I would not have to justify my impudent prying.

Muriel opened the door so that the justification that was on the tip of my tongue rolled silently across the floor.

'I need to see Mr Sargent,' Roger de Lacy said and he never lifted his ear trumpet to hear her response nor did he turn to acknowledge her presence. Instead he reached towards the bookcase and took from the third shelf down a copy of 'Temple Bar'. There must have been two hundred of those volumes in those six shelves, all green leather and gold plated titles.

'The journal of the eighteenth century,' he said, giving it to me to hold.

That volume opened by itself at the page that told of the defeat of Napoleon at the Battle of Waterloo. And as I stood there looking at that opened book I felt the very breath of time breathing down my neck. An old smell, like when my tongue was all white and fur like, like when I licked the back of my hand and smelt my lick, it was like that, it was Roger de Lacy standing behind me and I could not move because it was his house and I was trapped in his smell, holding his book.

Then I wanted to tell him the history of our family of how we came with Napoleon's brother and then it dawned on me that then we were the beaten, just like all those German and Italian prisoners up at the camp. I remembered how glad I was that I was English when my Dad had said the morning he'd captured the German, that them lot was beat up at the camp, that's why they did not just pack up and go home because they was beat. When he'd said that I was glad that I was English. But looking at the pages of that book I felt angry that once we, my family, were the beaten.

The part of that book that opened in my hand in that room was the description of the journey to London from Broadstairs. The news of that victory. Of how the ship had been becalmed in mid Channel and how they had been rowed ashore by oarsmen and then the speeding carriage with the captured French eagles and standards poking out of the windows so that they could be laid at the feet of the Prince Regent in London. And all the time I was reading Roger de Lacy was breathing down my neck, it felt as if he himself with all his breeding was laughing at me because he did not know who I was because I was nothing but the gas man's brat. It was then I wanted to tell him how our names should be spelt. All that spelling sort of concentrated all my thoughts and I saw in my mind Roger de Lacy, the man breathing down my neck, his name and I saw that it was a French name. That book was heavy, yes, heavy, as heavy as all the history it contained.

As I felt Roger de Lacy's hand lift off my shoulder he said to me, 'We have to keep the curtains drawn,' he said, 'it stops the leather from fading.'

The time had gone when I should have told him those things that I knew about my name.

And then there was a rustling as the curtains moved and the room turned grey as it became embraced in a duller light, me still holding that heavy book and my breathing disturbing the limits of audibility.

The problem that he wanted to see my father about was that there was a smell of gas in his bathroom.

I have never seen a bathroom like Roger de Lacy's bathroom. It was installed in the corner of the biggest bedroom that you can ever imagine. This bedroom was so big that you could play any ball game in it. In fact there was an old dried milk tin lying on its side together with half a dozen golf balls around the mouth of the tin. These were all in the centre of a great Turkish carpet. And there was a four poster bed in that room that had red velvet curtains hanging so that you could draw them and make your own private room. But the curtains were open and the bed was all littered with the tiredness of the night before. It seemed that there were no wardrobes in the room, no cupboards that could contain clothes and then I saw that there were brass handles on the oak panelled walls so that those handles told me where the wardrobes were.

The bathroom had been built into the right-hand corner of the room. It looked as if someone had erected a lean-to green house there. The one side of the bathroom was glass and the great copper geyser stood in all its copper glory outside the bathroom. The thing was surrounded by a collection of copper pipes, and there was a pressure gauge on one of the pipes and there were little vapours of steam surrounding those pipes. It was almost like a steam engine, it hissed, it could be alive, it had a life of its own. Inside the bathroom itself there was an enamelled bath with giant lion's feet that gripped the white scrubbed wooden floor.

'It smells of gas,' Roger de Lacy said.

And then Dad was moving from inside of that bathroom to the outside where the geyser stood in all its splendour.

'It's the bypass,' Dad replied. And now he had additional limits imposed upon him so that as he moved behind the great apparatus he became empowered with knowledge that was in that instant superior to Roger de Lacy's. Muriel was watching him and so my Dad, my father that incorrigible improviser whose only dream was to act the fool on stage, started to perform and only now do I understand the boredom of an unfulfilled life that was at that time strangling him. He was like magic my Dad as he reached up and touched the tap that turned off the gas. And then with his little adjusting spanner he was turning a nut.

'You're lucky that there was not an explosion,' Dad shouted into Roger's trumpet.

'Hell', Roger shouted back trying to keep up with Dad who had now moved back into the bathroom so that he could turn on the hot water tap. And Roger following him and then doubling back so that they were back outside again.

'Gas,' Dad shouted into the trumpet. 'Look, it's not lit, leaking into the room.'

'Good God,' Roger shouted, doing a pirouette as he turned to face Dad.

'How long's it smelt like this ?'

'Months.'

'I've increased the size of the jet,' and every time Dad spoke he shouted into the brass ear trumpet so that both men were moving around the bath with the geyser and brass pipes that was built inside the oak panelled room with the great four poster bed.

It was a spontaneous movement that seemed to release emotions and then when Dad felt that Roger could not see him he held his ear like a trumpet so that Muriel started to laugh and then when he moved back to the bath to turn on the tap so that the flowing water started the geyser with almost an explosion ... he was walking like Groucho Marx ... large strides and both men almost running into each other

'So sorry,' Roger said.

'I thank you,' Dad said.

Saying the 'you' like Groucho whilst at the same time creating a drama of movement through the expressive use of his body. And all the time Roger de Lacy turning with his great cape swirling and then mutually exhausted they both stopped and old

Roger de Lacy pulled from beneath his coat a packet of Capstan full strength cigarettes and then Muriel and I watched the two men inhale and then exhale, both of them silently contemplating the blue smoke of the cigarettes.

This contemplation caused Roger de Lacy to turn to my father and ask him what was going on at the gasworks.

'Not much,' Dad replied.

'The great hole in the road, I saw it whilst passing in the car last week.'

And I saw the Lanchester limousine, with his chauffeur Jukes peacock-capped at the wheel sliding silently past, Roger de Lacy leaning forward shouting into the speaking tube ... a movement, like him now swinging around ear trumpet in hand towards my father for his response.

'IT'S A SCENTED PLANT,' Dad shouted into the ear trumpet.

'WHAT?'

'A SCENTED PLANT.'

'Good God'

'Lemon'

'WHAT?'

'DEPENDING ON THE AREA.'

'GOOD GOD'

'SO THAT WHEN THERE IS A LEAK REPORTED WE KNOW WHERE IT IS.'

'CAPITAL.'

'YES.'

'CAPITAL IDEA.

And they were both moving again, my father setting before our eyes the picture of someone phoning in to report a leak, no misunderstanding of where it was, scent-coded, him not bored, exuberant, sometimes lowering his voice, so that old Roger de Lacy was tapping his trumpet and shouting 'WHAT?' now and then. The splendid sudden scented gas invention which he had dreamed up turning into a dangerous but beautiful rash growing in front of the glass-sided bathroom that was now full of steam like a jungle hot house.

'Look!' Dad shouted, 'it works. You must make sure the bypass is turned up or it will blow out and if you don't watch out the bloody thing will do what Cromwell failed to do.'

'CROMWELL?'

'HE'S THE NEW RESIDENT ENGINEER.'

And then Roger de Lacy turned to leave the room, his coat swinging and swirling around his tall thin body as he shouted 'THERE'S A HALF CROWN ON THE SIDEBOARD FOR SARGENT.'

And Dad said to Muriel, 'The toffs are a constant blessing throughout the land. We'll have to head in the direction of the Charlton Arms, the Regulo needs final adjustment so's they can cook the Sunday joint.'

# 8 A Four Speed Gear Box

I was eating a boiled egg at a quarter to eight when the dog barked senselessly at the postman. There was one letter. It was addressed to my father. It was typed. It had a Chester post mark. My mother held it up to the light while I pushed soldiers into the egg yolks of our own brown eggs.

She would not open it, but she was curious and then the weather forecast said that it would rain, but it was already raining and I would have to wear wellies and I did not want to wear wellies because I would not be able to run in them, they were a size too big. I had to grow into them, everything I ever owned was bought a size too big so that by the time it was the correct size it was worn out. And then next door's toilet flushed and I had a loose tooth ... so I pushed a soldier that was part of the crust too hard. It broke through the bottom of the egg and then as I pulled it back it became stuck and the egg came out of the egg cup all over my trousers but my mother said nothing. She was still trying to see who had sent Dad a typed letter from Chester.

That letter was the beginning of laborious letter-writing for my father. It was about his aunt's will. She had caused much suffering to our family because the rest home up near Knutsford kept writing for money after her cash assets had been used up. Dad's old aunt had been suffering from senile dementia. She had all her life been housekeeper to a great lady in Knutsford. She had received most of her salary in shares in the Manchester Ship Canal. From what the solicitors said in the letter there was still a huge bill unpaid and what was more, it seemed that the rest of the family were suggesting that the house that we were living in had been built by Dad's aunt for her mother and so was in effect part of her estate and could be used to pay the debt. Not only that but it turned out that she had been persuaded to make the Church her trustee.

It was a nightmare. Our life was about to run out of control. Those people up north were suspect and burdened in greed.

'They'll not get a penny,' Dad was shouting.

'It'll not come to that.'

'The street, we'll be out on the street. Those buggers never come to visit. Not since before the war. And Sid's got plenty of money. Oh my God, Edna, I don't know what to do. It'll be the bloody workhouse.'

'No, John it will not come to that.'

And then I knew that there was something really serious happening, when they started using each other's Christian names. No one ever called Dad John, except Mother. Everybody knew him as Jack.

And then for three weeks Dad would peel an apple outside the back door after every meal and throw the core at the old damson tree.

'A letter from hell, signed by the devil,' and then 'FUCK IT,' he shouted. 'FUCK IT.'

And that was the first time that I'd ever heard him use that word, the worst word that anyone could ever use.

I was ten and told Mrs Poole that our house was

in a fucking mess. I told her that while I played with her grandson Frank who was spoilt by her. He had a train set and would only let me look at the engine, I could not even touch the thing. She was big in the church and marched me home after she had written on a piece of paper what I had said. The word was so bad that she could not say it.

'I'll get your mother to clean your mouth out with soap,' she said.

But my mother sent me up the garden to feed the rabbits until Dad came home. He could not find me. I was in the pigsty, hiding with the dog. The dog gave the game away. And then Dad did something that I will never forget. He came into the sty and sat down with me and said,

'It is a fucking mess, everything is in a fucking mess, but don't use that word outside this garden or when anyone else is listening. Better still, don't use it at all. It won't help.'

And then he kissed me on the head. 'I'm going to see Jock Slater,' he said, 'he'll sort it out.'

I knew then that typed letters were very serious, but I also knew that Jock Slater was our solicitor and was smart because even though he stuttered he was a solicitor.

It was one of those times when I felt that my Dad was thinking the exact same thoughts as me because Dad said after a very long pause, 'He don't stutter when he writes a letter.'

And then my father was smiling and when we came out of the pigsty the sky was all red and the sun was floating like a big red balloon and I held my Dad's thumb and we both watched the sun sink behind the church.

It all took more than six months to sort out. During that time mother lost herself in Chopin's

Nocturnes and by the time she came out of them the whole world started to get better and warmer. Mother decided that we would all go on a day trip to Barry Island.

Mr Timmis was organising the trip on his beloved Great Western Railway. He always called it the Great Western even though it had been nationalised and was now known as British Railways. It was strange, him being a Labour councillor and all, but that was how it was. Every school in our town went on a special train organised by him. We had to put our names down three weeks before the trip. The whole school was talking about it, everybody was going, we were going to see the sea. We had to draw what we thought the sea looked like. Someone had been to Worcester and seen ships on the river Severn, but the sea was even bigger than that because there were liners with as many passengers as there were people in our town and it was difficult for us to visualize that. It was incredible to think that there was a boat with funnels bigger than our church steeple, and ours was a fine great church, almost a cathedral.

It was the first time in my life that I measured days, the first time that I waited for a day to come. Those three weeks were a very long time.

And then it happened and I can remember seeing the sea for the first time in my life from the window of the train. The sea so big and so blue and the ships in the distance were so small, so small that I did not believe that they were as big as our church.

'Look at the gulls,' Mother said, 'there's the soul of a dead fisherman inside every one.'

And that was the last time I saw the sea because the tide was out when we got to Barry. Dad, Uncle Dicky and Mr Williams from next door went to search for a pub. We tried to make sand castles in sand that was like mud. There were thousands of people on that beach but there was no sea.

It was out there somewhere because my mother left us with Mrs Poole who had rolled her dress up above her knees and then Mother came back wet and dripping with all her hair hanging like rats' tails. She did not look like my mother and my sister started to cry and then Dad came back with Dicky and Mr Williams, they were all so full of beer that they had tied four knots in handkerchiefs and then placed them on their heads. We were halfway through the day and I was missing my dog and all they could do was to lie down on the sand and fart.

And then they wanted to pee and so Dad dug a hole with my red spade and then rolled on to it, and then rolled back and filled the hole up again. Dicky saw him do it and then did the same. Mrs Poole never saw them and she was only a few feet away. I was accused of getting sand into the cheese sandwiches, we drank cold tea, there was a rumour that there was ice cream for sale, but no one could find out where they sold it. My spade broke and then it was time to catch the train. That was the first time I went to the seaside and it didn't matter that there was no sea or that the ships were so small, our house was still our house and Dad was going to buy a motorbike.

It was the result of another typed letter, this time from Jock Slater. It seemed that the church whom Dad's aunt had made her trustee when she went senile had more than enough money left and what was more she had left her estate to her sister, my Dad's mother, who had died two months before I was born. She was the only one in our family to have had a portrait of herself painted in oils. It was in the sitting room and my father always put the first celandine that he found each spring in between the glass and the frame of her portrait. When he did that her face smiled, she became alive, and I became afraid of her.

Everything had turned out all right. We were to have an indoor toilet and bathroom. Dad was to have a greenhouse and there was enough left for him to buy a motorbike.

It was the answer to my father's prayer. A 1938 Triumph Speed Twin and because it was just after the war and there were massive shortages, he paid more for the thing than it cost new. Dad had to justify that. He said that the bike would enable him to do the journey from Tenbury in less than ten minutes. It took him three quarters of an hour normally, much longer if he called in to try one at the Rose and Crown. Uncle Dicky was a stoker at the Tenbury branch of the gasworks and Kelly Baker was a yard labourer. They all went to work on push bikes and they all came home on push bikes. But sometimes if it was raining they would call in at the Rose to try one. Sometimes if it looked like it might rain then they would call in and try one. Sometimes if the sky was blue and there was just one cloud then they would try one. If there were no clouds and it was a clear warm day then they would ease their thirst before they had one, just to be on the safe side. They were a good solid team. Whether or not my mother thought that the motorbike would break this team we shall never know, but she never made objection to Dad's proposal when he suggested that he should buy the machine. This worried him, so he reinforced his proposal by pointing out that if it was only to be a small flirtation with the beast then no matter, because if and when he sold it, he would get more than he had paid.

Anyway, it was mid July, and sudden waves of heat must have dissolved Mother's fears as she picked fine new potatoes from the top patch. And as if this was not enough, there were peas so tender that we ate them raw in salads of fresh lettuce, red radishes, beetroot and hard boiled eggs.

From noonday until evening that space of time collected the whole fire of those summer days until the bright blue sky exploded into white thin layers of cloud and we, my sister and I together with the dog, played naked underneath the old Cox's orange pippin, taking the heat of the sun to bed inside our bodies where it leaked like honeysuckle pulp.

The internal combustion engine had been invented some seventy or eighty years before Dad bought his motorbike. Uncle Dicky told Dad that while he was up in the shed drinking cider, he also told him that the first motorbike was made in 1869 by a man called Michaux who had a factory in Paris. This Frenchman had installed a small steam engine in the frame of a pedal-powered push bike.

Dad liked the idea that a Frenchman had been the inventor of the motorbike.

'It proves something,' he said to Dicky, and then they had to drink to it. My Dad and Dicky would drink to anything.

That was last weekend. Now we were all looking at the great machine standing on its centre stand.

'You said it was a French mon who invented the motorbike,' Dad said to Dicky as he kicked the front tyre.

'Aaahh,' Dicky said, 'and it was another Frenchmon that put the petrol engine into a three-wheel bike,' and I watched uncle Dicky roll a cigarette. 'Monsieur Georges Bouton was his name.'

'By God, Dicky, they are an inventive bunch, the French,' Dad said.

'Ah, they be'. And Dicky was taking the first draw and then he exhaled and said, looking at the motor-bike, 'It'll be the end of the push-biking to work then, Jack?'

'Ooooh, I dunno about that,' Dad said. 'We could always try one.'

'Naa, 'twon't be the same, anyway I'm thinkin' of gettin a car'. And then I looked at Dicky looking at the motorbike and Dad said nothing, he just threw his leg over the bike, pushed it off the centre stand and said, 'I'll start it for yer ... hell of a sound.'

And he must have flooded the thing because it would not start. No matter how many times he stood on the kick starter, it just would not start. After six or seven kicks he started to sweat and to go red in the face.

'Dunna sell the push bike yet,' Dicky shouted.

'Er always does this when somebody's watchin'.

And then with extreme effort Dad put all his weight onto the kick starter and there was an explosion about force six on the Richter scale which sent our dog and next door's dog into howling fits as the whole thing shook before coming to life and then Dad was moving a lever on the handlebar that sort of tamed the thing, until it settled down to a dull thump every second or so, and then Dicky and Dad were shouting over the thumping,

'Sounds well.'

'Four speed gear box, Dicky.'

And then Dad blipped the throttle so that there was a gathering together, all the thumps speeding up so that the sound was a powerful burble, and the boys next door came running round to listen to the sweetness of the thing and as it warmed up a thin blue smoke came out of the exhaust pipes and hung like a blue haze so that we all started coughing.

'THE RINGS,' Dicky shouted.

'RINGS?' Dad shouted.

'THE PISTON RINGS.'

And Dad looked at Dicky and Dicky looked back at Dad and my Dad realised that perhaps Dicky knew more about the internal combustion engine than he did.

Next Saturday afternoon Dad sat on a wooden box beside the innards of the Speed Twin. His hands covered in black engine oil, he explained to me how the chain had to be kept oiled and kept adjusted so that it ran at the correct tension and would not jump off, like it just had that morning when he was on his way back from Tenbury. The chain had jumped off because we had won the war and it was impossible to buy a new chain, all the metal in England having been used to make bombs and that was why I had to run up to Clive Wontner's with the dog because he had a chain that once belonged to a Rudge Whitworth motorbike. And so I ran up there and back with the thing all coiled up inside a sack like a dead snake.

But it was the wrong size and my father sat there cursing the fact that every motorbike had a different size chain, and that he had something useless and that he would have to buy Cocky a pint because he was so generous him giving him a useless chain that no one could ever want ...

Suddenly it flashed through his head that Mr Morgan the bee-keeper had a collection of old chains, having been an enthusiastic rider before the war and so I had to run up to his house. But he was busy keeping his bees down in the orchard, which was a half a mile away from his house.

'We'll have to go and see him then,' Dad yelled.

And so we went with the dog and left all the screws and the chain guard and the can of oil lying on the ground.

We could not see Mr Morgan, he was bending down at the back of his furthest hive. So Dad opened the gate to the orchard and there under the vaults of the trees one could see the hovering cloud of smoke that told the exact position of the bee-keeper, who was dropping a swarm into a basket hive.

Mr Morgan looked up when we entered and shouted,

'MIND THE BEE LINE!'

But because we did not know where the bee line was, we froze in our steps and looked about us like idiots listening to the song of a blackbird … together in that orchard criss-crossed with shafts of the sun and the song of a blackbird hanging continuously in the air and all Dad wanted was a chain for his bike, us not wanting to be the main characters in the scene of chaos that followed, late afternoon, in the month of July, one bee stinging Dad on the top of his head, the bald patch, and him running in all directions, the orchard all of a sudden filled with shameful words that I had never heard Dad say before, words that Mrs Poole would not be able to write on a piece of paper as the queen in the swarm of bees decided that the place that she was about to enter was not where she wanted to be.

Me petrified, glued to the spot, watching the cloud hovering above my head, a great golden constantly changing blob of vibrating wings, an ocean of sound above my head becoming more vivid as it peeled away towards where Dad was running, him with his leg on the top of the holly hedge struggling with his other leg, that great insect sound-sculpture moving towards where he had fallen, him taking his shirt off, stripped to the waist, running with rhythmic steps down the alleyway that separated the orchard from George Sanders' pigsty.

Oh yes, and what was more I was afraid to laugh because it was not what my Dad had intended to do, not like when he acted the fool just to make people laugh, what was happening was something else, a real tragedy.

So I told Mr Morgan that Dad wanted a chain and then walked home with the dog to find Dad standing over the bike with a sledge hammer, and being unable to smash the bike he instead started to smash the surface of the lawn. It was the only way that he could stop himself from smashing the bike that had been his for less time than it took to level that lawn when he had rolled it and spread the seed, and there he was making holes in what was our lawn. It was worse than when I'd dug little holes with a small trowel, these were great big holes and they were everywhere. He'd belted me across the ear for making my small holes, and now he was making great big ones and Mother was looking at him, rubbing her hands and not saying a thing because Dad's face was so full of the temper that was in him that even the dog stood with her tail between her legs. But that was not all: two-year-old Ted, who was the baby of a neighbour from up the road, had oil on his face and the screws that held the chain guard in place were missing. So next thing that happened was that Mum and Ted's mother were pushing him in a pram up to Doctor Hooker's, who told his mother to look in his turds every day for a week.

But eventually the bike did go and that was the

Sunday morning when the church bells were calling us. My Dad kicked the starter just once that morning, the engine bursting into life, the sound of the church bell drowned in the unique rhythm of the Triumph Speed Twin engine, vibrating in its frame like the heart of a living creature. My Dad with his cap backwards held in place by goggles, lifting me up onto a cushion strapped to the petrol tank. My hands on those handlebars, me leaning forwards, my legs tucked up so that my feet would not touch the exhaust pipes, the Triumph speaking louder as Dad twisted the accelerator and the only thing that I could see was the road going underneath the front wheel, unless I lifted my head which was near to the speedometer.

The speedometer, that black needle telling our velocity as we were projected into the still air between the hedgerows along the Overton Road. Dad and I in the bosom of the morning, the pattern of the road a blur beneath the front wheel as the speedometer moved slowly towards the six and the nought that told us that we were flying along that road at more than a mile a minute, which was faster than I'd ever been before. The wind streaming past my ears drowning out all other sounds as my Dad opened up the engine and catapulted us towards the policeman's corner which flew past, a blur, the old man in the garden gaping at a man and a child on a speeding motorbike, the child's head down almost touching the speedometer, unable to look ahead because of the battering wind in his face, only once opening his mouth, because of flies, and the warm engine thick with the smell of petrol, an experience that evoked within me a tantalising fascination for speed that would never leave me.

# 9    *A Green Cigar*

It was strange that I should have had a call to a
house one street away from my mother's house the
very same time as an ambulance was turning into
her drive. I saw that ambulance waiting and knew
that it was for her, that they would be taking her
away for the last time.

The fare who said that she was in a hurry for a
cab, was taking her time to come out of the house
and even asked me to wait so that she could phone
her friend to see if she was going to bingo.

'Make up your mind what you want,' I shouted
into her house. And then she started to get funny,
threatening to phone the local council to complain
about my attitude, which was burning inside me,
but she did not know why I was about to turn into a
mad house.

'You can phone the Duke of Edinburgh,' I
shouted back, and then the radio in the cab started
to buzz and I had a fare to pick up at the station,
the eight o'clock train, a stockbroker who lives in a
manor house underneath the hill, a man of means
who tips well, who knows where he is going, not to
be ignored, and still no movement from the bingo
maniac so I just drove away, wondering if she would
get through to Phil the Greek.

It was therefore after nine thirty when I finally

got to my mother with a nurse standing over her bed. There she lay, so small, propped up on six pillows, moving her head from side to side, moaning about the state of her backside which must have been hell for her, constipated for over two weeks, blocked. My mother, who used to give my sister and I syrup of figs every Friday night so that we were not let out to play on Saturday morning until we had been and what was more you were not allowed to pull the chain until she had seen the actual proof.

She lay in the bed under clean white sheets, looking directly ahead, staring almost fixedly at a vase of flowers fluttering in the stream of air from an electric fan. A steady rustling noise in the ward. Her eyes hardly recognising me, no longer expecting anything or anyone, her still blue eyes, like forget-me-nots, eyes whose life had almost stopped, given up because of a cursed lump of shit.

The nurse leaning over, lifting her up like a rag doll, her arms limp, white, her skin looking as if it had been washed in lime wash so that as I looked at her arm I looked at it in horror and disgust, her still staring at those flowers.

'Look who's come to see you,' the nurse said and Mother said nothing,

'It's your son,' the nurse added.

And then with great effort my mother said, 'I can see who it is ... he should be at work, not wasting time here.'

And then my mother sort of shivered. It was as if she knew that she would never shit again, that stone in her bowel was the final solution and she bent her hands, those hands that had once played her violin, long delicate hands that she used to protect with very expensive cream, hands that now had a thin transparent skin so that I could see all her veins and her knuckles and her fingers were twisting in on themselves, those hands that had once held me, those hands that could not now even hold a cup of tea.

I leant forward and held those hands and they were cold, corpselike, and I looked round in that room at all the other beds there and it was as if I was looking at the very edge of fate and I thought then that my mother must have been constantly hungry for the last few months, her refusing to eat, her reasoning that it was the only way to get rid of that constipated feeling.

I felt myself stroking her hands, feeling her bones, feeling the softness of her thin skin and I looked at the silhouetted shapes of the nurses behind the curtained beds and they looked like hooded ravens waiting, and I felt myself choking as she looked up at me:

'You should be at work. Do it while you can,' she said.

And so I drove round town sobbing, trying to please my mother for the last time, but in reality I was sobbing because I wanted to escape from her.

Her smell.

She smelt as if she was turning rotten. It was as if she was decomposing in her bed. I was therefore thankful that she had asked me to leave so that I could justify my leaving by saying to myself that I was obeying her last wish. So there I was racing around town until three am while my mother lay in our little hospital with a stone trapped in her bowels like some rat of decay.

'Goodnight,' my boss said.

And I was unable to answer, unable to tell him about the knife inside me.

Next day the wind kept the clouds scudding

across the sky so that as I walked up towards the centre of town shadows were continually moving, the sun chasing shadows, shadows chasing the sun, and all I wanted was a green cigar just like my father used to make, rolling the green leaves across his thigh:

'Like the women in Cuba do,' he used to say, 'they makes the best cigars in the world'.

And his cigars were rolled just like that. He even rolled his trousers up so that he had bare thighs.

'That's how they do it,' he said, 'that's the way, the same way that they does it in the tobacco factories in Cuba.'

And it was a fact that the leaves stuck together better when he rolled them on his naked thigh. It never worked as well when he had his trousers on, the leaves would sometimes unroll. My Dad and his books and his belief in Pataphysics, the science of imaginary solutions, him with that imaginary vision of Cuban women rolling tobacco on naked thighs. My Dad who had never lost sight of the church tower in his life except for one day trip to London where he got lost and then asked a policeman if he had seen any of the Ludlow gang, a policeman who looked at him as if he were daft.

'Is it market day?' Dad asked.

'It's like this all the time,' the policeman replied.

'To hell with a tale like that,' Dad said. 'There's thirty from the gasworks here for a start.'

So that day I felt as if I wanted a green cigar and I looked everywhere for a green cigar or any other good big cigar, but there are no longer any tobacconists in our town, no one anymore bothers about what they smoke, our race has lost all its taste and it's got worse since the cattle market has moved out of town so that now you can no longer tell if it is

114

market day or not. In fact that morning I could, if I wished, have let both barrels of Dad's old four ten shotgun blast out along the high street and not even hit a dog. Like a desert, it was, at something past nine, no morning promenade and there would be no evening promenade either. It was as if the town had passed away. And I thought about what it was once like with the London Tea Company just selling tea, all those different smelling leaves, different tastes, for people who once had taste, in a shop that is now selling second hand clothes that would have once been sold for a few pence in a rummage sale.

Rummage sales, sales of cast offs that raised hundreds of pounds for the Labour Party, for all the different churches that were once in our town, the Wesleyans, the Baptists, the Congregationalists, the Methodists, the Primitive Methodists, the Anglican Church, the Roman Catholic Church, all those churches that once laid on outings to the seaside, to the pantomimes and the Christmas tea parties so that the poor used to belong to as many churches as they could and go to as many parties as they could because it was the only time in their life that they ate jelly or blancmange or had cakes. All those parties gone. Like the town hall, demolished because it did not look right. Our town hall with its sprung dance floor, the fancy dress balls and the grand dances with great bands like Ken Mackintosh and his Orchestra and all the women dressing up in ball gowns and the young ones twisting the night away in skirts so short that there was nothing left to imagine except that you could see all those muscles working away in those parts that were like marble pillars, so smooth and large that you could only imagine what would happen if those legs were to open wide and when the Jeffs girl danced with Aggi Shepherd and did the splits there was nothing more to imagine.

All gone.

When there were concert parties, and my mother playing the violin and Dad making people laugh. When so many people played an instrument that they could have made two symphony orchestras and even though they played sometimes badly the sight of all those instruments being played, the movement of it all like a dance, a drawing together almost a physical response.

All gone.

Like the two cinemas closed down and old Mary Ann sitting in the front row shouting;

'LOOK OUT HE'S BEHIND YOU, YER SILLY BASTARD' and then throwing a beer bottle at the screen because the wrong cowboy got shot.

All gone.

I really felt that time had stopped that morning. It was as if I was looking in the rear view mirror in a car and not looking where I was going and all I wanted was a green cigar. It was as if that morning everything had fallen into a state of slumber, as if our town had swallowed a poisoned apple and I wanted to go back home and get out of my car and ride to Shrewsbury just to get a green cigar and would have if I could have been sure that I could have got a green cigar in a tobacconist's there. But I was not sure that I could get a green cigar even in a city like Shrewsbury. I was trapped because my mother had that morning lost all the strength and courage to live. I knew that she would never go home again ...

So it was no surprise when my sister phoned to tell me that Mother was dead.

'She died eating a spoonful of blancmange,' my
sister said.
It felt so strange to listen to that news
me a civilised white man of the twentieth century
holding an ear piece to my ear
not able to see the whites of my sister's eyes
not able to share sorrow

the phone's inability to capture the substance of
silence
'are you still there,' she said
but I could not answer
me in the centre
of it all
realising that it can
disappear
very quickly
oh my sister
I would have liked
to have held you then
it would have been
better to have kept the news

Three days later. It was Thursday but it could
have been Sunday, it felt like a Sunday, my wife and
I looking at the corpse of my mother inside the
funeral parlour.

We were alone in that room and I didn't know
how long to stay, with the corpse of my mother.
What was the expected time to remain in there?

A closed room, no windows, tomb-like, airless,
you could not hear any noise from outside, just
some kind of background music, a buzzing, that was
all, and as I looked at my mother I could not help
thinking about that lump of crap still in her bowel.

She looked wax-like but her eyes had sunken and

she ought to have smelt but there was no smell, just the air, heavy like lead, which wouldn't let us breathe. My wife standing next to me and then I could not remember where the door was. I turned, still holding my wife's hand, and saw that the door was directly behind me. It reassured me, the knowledge that the door was behind me and then I got the impression that my mother was too small for the coffin, that they had somehow lifted her up so that she floated on a bed of tissue paper.

'Do it while you can,' were the last words that she said to me and I didn't know whether to laugh or cry.

My mother who would have liked to be buried without any priest, just put in a hole, a deep hole without any ceremony …

'Without any mumbo jumbo,' she would have said.

And then she looked more peaceful in her coffin. All of a sudden her face took on a restful and serene look. It was as if in her box she had settled down like a cat in her proper place, as if she had found my weakness, that weakness being that I would bury her as near as possible, in as normal a way as possible, to what would be an acceptable way in our society, when in all honesty all she wanted was to have been dropped in a hole without …

Without even a coffin.

One month later I am in my mother's house, her walls the space between those walls all those objects, important things collected during her life, buoys, points of reference, useless things to us but important meanings to my mother, a collection of photographs, dead uncle Wilf, once a scrum half, a coal miner, I saw him cleaned and scrubbed in a fireside tub a big man, silicosis, hopeless, I once put on his miner's hat.

'You idiot, get that thing off yer head if ever I see you with one of them things on yer head I'll break both yer legs' and he meant it.

A sort of single settee that folds out to make a bed. Her sideboard's oak, an antique, and the walls are a sort of cream, between them hovers her smell, the remains of her, perhaps a little musty so the door is open, back and front and a current of air, for the first time ever, the back door and the front door open together, a current of air wafting through her house, taking away with it her smell.

Tomorrow they will come to take her things away. My sister and I don't want much. We have taken all that we think that we need, those small things that we think will remind us of her, just the big stuff is left, the furniture, the TV, the table, the chairs, the sofa. I would have liked to have taken it all, instead I memorise the room. The walls cream, the ceiling white, someone else will paint the walls a different colour. We will sell her house. We should burn it, like the gypsies used to do, we should have a big fire and burn all her possessions and we should have thrown her on the top and burnt the lot and we should have celebrated as we did it.

All the time I am in her house I can hear a kind of buzzing sound. My mother's house should be completely silent, she had double glazing fitted so there should be just silence but there is instead a kind of buzzing. It could be the electric night storage heaters, but it feels more than that, it feels like some kind of energy, it reminds me of the noise that a fax makes, it sort of comforts me. For a moment I feel that my mother has made a journey back, I have the feeling that she is free from her human form and is wandering about like a liberated e-mail letter.

Suddenly as if a whirlwind had set itself down in the centre of the house both the doors slam shut.

I am not afraid.

I walk into her bedroom and see that a pile of old magazines has fallen over. Where they have fallen I see her old scrapbook lying open on the floor. The page that is open has pasted into it the front page of 'Psychic News'. It is dated Thursday 27th September 1975. The article is about spirit communication using a tape recorder. There is a photograph of a man called Friedrich Jurgenson wearing headphones operating an old reel to reel tape recorder. A strange looking man with an intense but kind face, the discoverer of the electronic voice phenomenon also know as Raudive voices. And then as I turned the pages of my mother's scrapbook I found another cutting, this time it was from the local paper, it was all brown and faded ...

'Jesus,' I said to myself, 'It's Rhoda,' Aunt Rhoda ... but she wasn't an aunt she was like Uncle Dicky was to Dad, she was mother's best friend. And the newspaper cutting was from that time in the history of my mother and father and Aunt Rhoda and Uncle Dicky, it was just that Mum and Dad got married and Aunt Rhoda and Uncle Dicky had not and the brown faded cutting in my hand was perhaps the reason why.

... *I would imagine that this young Lady and the prisoner of war became infatuated. You may not admire her taste but you cannot control love. But it is an offence that there should be more than friendliness between these two. Some Italians have love making ways with them which women of this country do not understand because they have not experienced such things before. It is a fearful ordeal for a girl to experience ...*

And then the cutting was ripped so that I could not read what had happened to the couple who must have been lovers. I felt then that the buzzing in my mother's house was her thoughts, my mother who was so tender that she could pass through walls by just sighing. I felt then in her house that she had at last become a divided being, that she had now come to terms with her spiritual longings. It was then that the continual buzzing became a wall of sound that was centred in the very roof of her house so I started to look for a step ladder and remembered that she had one in her shed.

And then I was afraid that I would find up in her roof a virtual chamber of wonders, so I paused before I opened the trap door, confused by sounds that invaded my imagination, sweating like a mad bull.

When I opened the trap door I found that the ballcock in the roof was still running when it should not have been, because it was me, me myself last week who had turned off the stop cock. And then when my head and shoulders were up in the darkness of her roof that waterfall of sound shrank, it became transformed into a dribbling but there was still an energy up there, an energy that made me feel about between the joists so that when I found my mother's old black violin case it was like an electric shock, and then the dribbling became like a long echo, a delay, and then it stopped.

There was one string left on my mother's violin.

There was no bow.

# 10   *Double Concerto*

So here I am standing in front of my mother's wardrobe looking at myself in the mirror, in the middle of the year 1996 looking more and more like my father. Thinking about how it was back then, feeling that since my father's death that I have become more and more like him, me changing into a reincarnation of my Dad.

Simple things like the way I now spit, how I clear my throat, when I smoke his pipes, just like he did. And how sometimes when I meet older people they will miss a generation and call me 'Jack', even talking about things that he did so that sometimes if they are very old I never bother to correct their error.

Here I am looking again at the scrapbook in my hand and that old faded cutting from so long ago, that piece of paper linking me to the past.

There used to be a sawmill opposite our house. During and just after the war it used to operate all night long. Our street was hemmed in, it was surrounded by the shattering sounds of steel blade saws cutting through wood. Twenty-four hours a day that sawmill worked. At night it was all lit up like a Christmas tree. Our house was shrouded in light and sounds.

My mother used to have to escape from those

sharp layered echoes. She used to play her violin on Thursday afternoons at Doctor O'Brien's. Doctor O'Brien was a graduate of Dublin University and had a Doctorate in music. I did not know that it was possible to be a Doctor in anything except medicine until my mother explained to me that a person with a Doctorate was someone who had been awarded a high academic degree in any field of knowledge.

'So,' my father said, interrupting my mother, 'You can have a doctorate in Pataphysics or cider drinking.'

That was when my mother kicked my father right across his shin, when he picked her up and threw her over his shoulder. It was when the dog bit my father. It was when he retreated up to his shed to continue his studies into the law of Pataphysics, the science of imaginary solutions.

Doctor O'Brien believed that music was developed from adult speech. He said that music was originally used to attract the attention of a potential mate.

'It was the rhythm,' he said.

Doctor O'Brien used to teach the piano. Everyone in Ludlow had a piano in the front room and there were three piano-tuners. The best one was blind. Doctor O'Brien was the best piano teacher. He could be observed moving from pupil to pupil with the aid of an enormous Armstrong Siddeley sit-up-and-beg push bike. He used to mount this bike with the aid of a step that stuck out from the rear axle. He used to employ the running and scooting method of mounting, running a little before scooting along and then easing himself up and over and into the saddle.

He always wore a hard bowler hat. His head was bald, it resembled a cracked hard boiled egg. The only time that you ever saw his head was when he was conducting the local orchestra. Then if he wanted the orchestra to drive into a certain melody he would lower his head and butt into it.

Doctor O'Brien lived in a large Victorian house that sat on the side of Tinkers Hill and overlooked the river. He had a black grand piano in his music room. The music room had French windows that led into a long conservatory where there was a lemon tree that grew green lemons.

At that time in the history of our town there were 3000 American troops, 1000 German prisoners of war and 500 Italian prisoners of war in the area. The strange thing was that it was the Americans who were the foreigners. I suppose that that was because they had more of everything than anyone else. Their uniforms were better and because they were used to having their clothes cleaned and pressed they felt frustrated when they could not find a dry cleaner in our town. So they drove around town in jeeps looking for women to clean those immaculate uniforms. All the women down our street used to earn extra money cleaning and pressing their clothes. Those that cleaned and pressed American uniforms could earn more than their husbands sent home to them from the front. Some women had strange feelings when they cleaned and pressed those American GI's trousers ...

The Germans had nothing except their pride. They used to make rope slippers and sell them from door to door. The Italians used to work on the land, alongside the Land Army girls. Rhoda was a Land Army girl. She came from Liverpool and she played the violin. Giuseppe played the violin, my mother played the violin, Hans Krebbers played the oboe and my Dad played almighty hell when he learnt that these four all played together in Doctor O'Brien's music room.

Dad bred rabbits, he had at any one time 60 rabbits in hutches all around our garden. He used to kill them and send the pelts to the RAF to make linings for airmen's leather jerkins. Dad fed them on bran mash, roots, kale, stale bread, and what he called the gatherings. We went out to get the gatherings from the side of the road. In those days there were lush verges each side. The back roads even had grass growing down the middle. The back road from Ludlow to Tenbury was like that, little used by cars. It had more than a mile of good well-kept verges, you could start a few hundred yards from our house gathering the roadside vegetation for a mile, then turn back and return down the other side of the road. In effect, there were two miles of verges, all ours. 'Street farmers,' Dad said we were. I would hold the sack and Dad would gather the grass and clover with his hands.

'You grasp it uth yer hand like a cow does uth er tongue,' he used to say, 'and then yer grazes like, uth yer hand'. And it worked. Dad could graze faster than a cow could eat. He could gather a sack of good grass and clover in under an hour.

That was how he taught me about herbs. Comfrey, garlic, meadowsweet, celandine, and hemlock.

'That's the one they gave to Socrates,' Dad said, 'killed him jead.' And all the time Dad would be pulling the grasses and I would be holding the sack.

Foxglove: 'Good if you got a bad heart, bad if you got a good un ... that's vetch and there's wild parsley and that's a good thistle, rabbits like a good thistle.'

But the thistles used to hurt my hands, but not Dad's hands. They were hard hands, good honest hands.

And that was how we met Dr O'Brien. We were gathering from the side of the road, him on his upright bike with come-to-Jesus handlebars, he who had to stop for the crack, he who would always fish about in his right hand pocket until he found two bent Players Weights cigarettes because he used to buy them by the weight, an ounce and a half of cigarettes at a time, from old Wainwright the tobacconist, and he would put them in his pocket, later to put both in his mouth and then fire them up and then offer one to whoever he was about to talk to and if he could only find half a cigarette then he would fire that up and all the remains would sometimes come out of his pocket so that he would say, 'It's a filthy habit.'

And then Dad was tackling him, that's what Dad used to call it, 'I'll tackle him about it,' he used to say. And so Dad was tackling Doctor O'Brien about having a German and an Italian and Mother with Rhoda all together in his music room.

'Jesus Christ almighty, will yer calm down now, Jack,' and Doctor O'Brien was lighting two crumpled cigarettes just like he always did, offering one to my father once he'd fired them both up.

'Will yer listen, Jack. It's the vibrations, there's more subtle vibrations in them dare instruments than what you can imagine, so close to the body those vibrations might be. There is a relationship between them vibrations and the human body, sound and vibrations are one and the same thing, it's energy, Jack, pure energy, a coming together, as it were.'

'No good will come of it,' Dad said.

'I'm always there.'

'I know but ...'

'Listen, Jack,' and Doctor O'Brien had removed his hat and was mopping his head with an old handkerchief and as he spoke there were furrows in his forehead and as he leaned his head back there were furrows in the back of his neck and his eyes started to swell.

'There is so much hatred in this place,' he began, and then his words started to tumble out of his mouth, 'and all them men trapped up in them there camps because they lost the war, which was not of their making, but more the shenanigans of a collection of leaders who have lost the ability to communicate one with the other, moreover I now can start to believe that the music will help them face the ferocity of a town that has lost so many of their kin.'

I stood listening to Dr O'Brien and noticed that he had small leather straps around the hubs of his wheels. When I moved closer to his bike he said to me, 'Keeps them clean, cat's collars, keeps them clean.' And then he said to Dad, 'How's yer syncopation coming along?'

And Dad said as he reached the last puff of his cigarette, 'Fine', and he nodded, flicking his cigarette away with the back of his thumb.

'Oh hell,' said the Doctor, 'come up to the house and I'll show you something that has been sent over from America by my brother who is working directly in the music business over there.'

And that was how I saw the black grand piano that you could see your face in. That was how I heard for the first time the music of Fats Waller. When Dr O'Brien hit the keys on his black grand piano, when his fingers began to leap along the keyboard, I couldn't take my eyes off those fingers stopping and then leaping again and him leaning forward so that his bald head shone and his eyes were large like when he was driving the local orchestra into the melody, but this time he was not struggling, he was playing and he was smiling and the room was full of notes, so many notes that they hung there and then he stopped dead and all ... all that was left was notes still ringing in my ears. And then the Doctor was opening a bottle of whisky and pouring into two small glasses and asking my father to play and then there was a horrible moment ... my Dad was struggling with that great piano.

'Do not overpower it,' the Doctor was shouting. 'Here have another tot.'

And then my Dad began to relax and fell out of his shell of self-doubt and his ramshackle tinkling became an expression of bliss so that I was very proud of my Dad playing Doctor O'Brien's great black piano and I looked at my Dad's hands and the Doctor's hands and I saw that the Doctor's hands were white and soft and were those of a man who earned his living differently to my Dad.

I never knew whether it was Dad playing that piano or the sheet music with Fats Waller's face and the words 'Ain't Misbehavin' that Dr O'Brien gave to my Dad or perhaps it was the whisky that changed his attitude to those four playing together but after that Dad spent a lot of time playing Fats Waller's music and he used to lift his right hand high in the air and wiggle his fingers before he hit the keys on our piano and then he had the idea that he could change the sound of the piano by pushing drawing pins into the hammers. That was too much for Mother who had just had the piano tuned by the blind man. So Dad did it to the piano in the pub where the Americans used to drink. And then came home so drunk that the dog found him on the lawn trying to lift the sheets over his body with his left arm.

'Things are moving fast,' he was murmuring as Mother was lifting him.

'It's the sun,' he mumbled as he struggled up the stairs, 'it's burning so fast that time is getting shorter.'

That happened the week before the sawmill burnt to the ground. It happened in the middle of a Sunday night. I knew that there was something wrong when I saw yellow fingers dancing on the ceiling. It was as if candle wicks were burning, there were constantly palpitating shadows playing, then everything became sharply illuminated and my mother rushed into my bedroom with my sister crying in her arms.

'It's all right,' she said.

But it was not all right. And then I saw that Mum and Dad's bedroom was flooded in a dense dazzling light and that Dad was looking out of the window. He was leaning on the window dressed in only his pyjama top. He looked strange. His backside was so white, he was scratching his bum watching the sawmill burning.

The great shed was burning, the offices were burning, the lead guttering was running down the down spouts like silver water and the down spouts were disintegrating into themselves and then running silver water across the concrete yard. We stood there in the front bedroom watching a downpour of roaring light and all the time my mother hugging me and stroking the back of my head.

'It's a bomb, Jerry's dropped a bomb,' Dad shouted.

'Don't be silly,' Mum said, 'the war's been over six months.'

'Oh ah,' Dad said, still scratching his bum, 'by gum it's a good thing.'

'Oh dear,' and then mother sighed a long deep sigh.

'It'll stop that infernal noise,' Dad said, 'it's the best thing that's happened down this street since the end of the war.'

And then Dad started to scratch his balls and smell his fingers.

'You got some filthy habits,' said Mother.

'Oh, bugger,' Dad shouted, 'look the paint's blistering on the windows.'

And then we all stood looking at the paint blister on the front bedroom windows. It was just like when Mr Tristam came down to paint the house, when he removed the paint with a blowlamp, when the paint became bubbles. It was just like that. As our paint blistered we heard the bell on the fire engine.

'Silly buggers', and Dad was laughing. 'Why on earth they want'a ring the bell at this time of night, there's nobody in the way.'

And from the landing we could see the tender with all the hoses curled up and the wooden wheels on the extending ladders spinning, ladders that could reach the highest building in our town, but not the steeple, 'God looks after that,' Fire Officer Baker once said. And he knew, because he had been to every fire in our town for the last 35 years. It was him that had warned the firemen when they were about to squirt the last part of the blaze on the Portcullis Inn,

'Dunna do that,' he shouted, 'we won't see what we'm doin.'

And now that red tender was racing down the

road towards us, firemen hanging on like grim death and all the time my father laughing.

'It'll be like pissing into a furnace,' he said.

By the time they'd arrived at the gate the flames were wrapping themselves around the steel girders that once held up the roof, a roof that now looked like a burning skeleton, the backbone of a great dinosaur. The twin iron gates were supported by stone pillars with jagged fragments of green glass embedded in the top glittering in the flames like jewels on a crown and all the time those firemen trying to open those gates that were chained together with a heavy chain.

'It's locked,' Dad said

'A fool can see that,' Mum said and Dad was still scratching his balls.

'I wish you'd stop that,' she said.

But Dad was concentrating on what the firemen were doing. And what they were doing was trying to open the steel gate but the heat from the fire must have been hotter down there than it was on the side of our house. Fire Officer Baker was now waving his arms about in all directions.

'He's going to tell them to get the hoses out,' Dad said.

And that was what the fireman did and when that hose came to life there was a great geyser gushing out of its end and Captain Baker was waving his arms and then they turned that great gushing hose onto the fire tender itself.

'The paint must be blistering on the fire engine,' and Dad was getting a little excited.

'How do yer know that?' said mother.

'If it's blistering up here then it must be like hell down there,' Dad said. 'Stupid woman'.

'What was that you said?' mother said.

'What's happening now is that they got so near the fire that the heat is evaporating the petrol before it gets into the engine and they can't back away ... where's me trousers?'

'Where you took em off.'

'Me trousers.'

'By the bed.'

'Me underpants?'

'Never mind about that', and Mum was shouting to Dad to come to the window.

'Look,' she said. 'What are they doing?'

'Trying to move the fire engine back onto the road.'

And there were four firemen holding a white blanket in front of the fire engine so that three men pushing the engine were sheltered from the heat of the flames and all the time Fire Officer Baker was gesticulating to the other two firemen holding the hose, to turn down the pressure so that they might be sprayed instead of battered about the place.

'You are now witnessing an extraordinary incident,' Dad was crowing. 'You can now see our fire brigade endeavouring to prevent themselves and their tender catching fire. If Baker's brains was made of dynamite then he wouldn't have enough to blow his hat off.'

And then there was a tremendous explosion as the roof on the building caved in on itself and a cloud of white hot ashes billowed into the sky so that a kind of darkness momentarily eclipsed the scene and when the soot and dust settled it looked as if it had snowed. And then from out of that cloud the figures of the firemen dancing around the fire tender and Fire Officer Baker stretching out both his arms so that the two firemen still squirting that great geyser let him have the full jet of it, the force of the water propelling him back against the still unopened gate.

It was so peaceful after the fire that we could not sleep. The empty space where once there was a sawmill was suspended in silence.

'That silence is too harsh,' my mother said.

And so she started to listen to the wireless once again. The Third Programme: Bach, Beethoven, Mozart, Haydn, Sibelius, Brahms, Wagner. Our house holding the rhythms and harmonies of those great composers and sometimes from the Light Programme the melancholy jazz ballads of my beloved Fats Waller, that large round fat black man who played Harlem stride piano, that's what Dr O'Brien said it was.

In the evenings Rhoda started to come frequently to our house. Rhoda asking my mother, 'Are you optimistic?'

'Mystic.'

'Psychic.'

'Psychomystic', Rhoda laughing as she moved around my mother's tailor's dummy with pins in her mouth.

'I'm more fatalistic, if it's meant to happen then it will happen'.

That was my mother's favourite saying.

'Anyway,' she said to Rhoda. 'You can't go back there, you'd be a foreigner out there, and Dicky's nice, kind, reliable.'

'It's all over with Dicky,' Rhoda said.

It amazed me how my mother and Rhoda could walk round that tailor's dummy all the time talking with pins in their mouths so that I was afraid what would happen if one of them swallowed one of those pins, me imagining that the swallowed pin would puncture their tummies and then they would bleed to death, finally drowning in their own rising blood. Secretly I wanted that to happen because they were always shouting at me not to put marbles into my mouth and I so liked the feel of that round-ness, it was so perfect a shape, rolling around my tongue and one day Rhoda told me that I must never ever swallow chewing gum, and that if I did then the innards in my stomach would stick together. When I did accidentally swallow a great wad of gum I ran upstairs to bed afraid to tell my mother in case she took me up to Dr Hunter (who was a surgeon so you had to call him Mr), Mr Hunter who had his own beds in the Cottage Hospital. He who told Dad when he had terrible pains in his side to go up to the hospital and tell Matron that he would be up to cut it out in the afternoon.I was afraid of Mr Hunter and his knife so I sat there waiting to become all gummed up, looking at that ceiling all afternoon just waiting ...

Some days my mother had to go to the dress shop to fit the customers with dresses that did not fit in the first place. It was that time when clothes were made to measure, when the customer was always right, when I was a nuisance waiting in the back room with my sister who was in a cot, a perfectly pleasant child who never cried, me bored, restless, unable to understand why my mother had to work or why my mother cried when she found that the coal bill could not be paid.

Sometimes if I was lucky Rhoda would look after me. That would be on Thursdays. She would ride my mother's bike with me sitting in the little seat over the back wheel, holding her violin case on my knees. Rhoda, her long black hair flowing, lifted above my head in the wind like a horse's tail, so that when she came to the hill it fell behind her back and brushed my face. Rhoda, her with the short cut nails of a girl who worked the land, her with the soft fur-like moustache above her upper lip that you could only see if she drank milk, her with the hairs under her armpits that smelt like Mrs Barr's goat, her who that morning when we arrived at the gate of Doctor O'Brien's kissed Giuseppe like my father kissed my mother on Saturday nights. Him waiting there behind that long five bar gate with the wire netting so that the two Irish terriers could not escape, him who always wanted a shave. Me trying to escape from that child seat that was too small for me, so that I could run into the back room of that house and find the long O gauge Hornby locomotive and place it on the tin plate track and wind up the clockwork motor and watch those pistons and valves working, moving in and out just like the real thing.

That day the violins seemed to move into each other. Sometimes her violin was almost silent and then the vibrations from his joined together with hers so that they were one with the other. Wave after wave, each more tender than the last, me standing in that doorway, the two of them moving into each other's sound, her hair flowing whilst she was bowing, the sounds almost silent, deeply coming, waves rolling, his almost black eyes crying, she looking away from him, her eyes puddled with tears, and all the time those droning strings so strong in the surrounding silence. Fragile sounds, disintegrating as they rolled across the floor overwhelming me, me almost ten years old watching, them, bowing, swaying, playing together in Doctor O'Brien's conservatory next to the green lemon tree.

'I have never heard it played like that,' said

Dr O'Brien with his hand resting on my shoulder, 'I have never in my life heard Johann Sebastian Bach's Concerto for Two Violins played like that, the second movement a work of true genius. We'll have to drink to it', and then the Doctor was pouring out his whisky into small glasses and I saw that the two handkerchiefs that Giuseppe and Rhoda had placed between their chins and the instruments that they had just played were soaking wet.

It was Thursday the following week, late in the afternoon, Rhoda and I riding through the centre of town with me holding her black violin case, when three women called out: 'Wop lover'.

It was the first time that I was to hear the ferocity of a town that was surrounded by hatred. It was not the last. All those women in our street who pressed the trousers of the American GI's, whose husbands were conscripted, looked at us as we cycled through town. The hissing whisperings coming loudest from those with American seeds hatching in their wombs. Rhoda pedalling harder and holding my hand when we walked and me asking when we could go out to Doctor O'Brien's so that I might play with the locomotive, because we had only been back once since I stood in that doorway, and then Giuseppe was not there and all the time Dr O'Brien saying,

'In the name of the blessed Virgin Mary, God if something goes wrong it's because there was something unforeseen. It is a dull country, this part in particular.'

And all the time him drinking from his whisky bottle and pulling his braces with his thumbs so that they flew back onto his chest with a wap and then Rhoda crying in the arms of Dr O'Brien, his wrinkled bald head sweating because of the whisky.

'One takes precautions,' she was sobbing.

'Tis all bollocks,' he said.

And then after a very long silence during which time I had wound the locomotive up three times, Dr O'Brien guided Rhoda to a dining chair and then pulling one across for himself, sat facing her.

'Tis a hard life,' he was saying. 'Some of us have instrumental skills and other poverty struck bastards have nothing, philistines, bog trotters, call them what you will, but I suppose that it was because of me that you will, if things turn out for the worse, have to endure the martyrdom of … oh shite where's me fags?' and him searching in his pockets for two cigarettes just like he did for my father and lighting them and as Rhoda smoked she said,

'These are strong. I feel giddy.'

'Players Weights,' he said. 'Good strong tobacco.'

Two days after that there was a knock at our door and Detective Sergeant Morris pushed his way in and all the time our dog barking and Mother for the first time not telling the dog to stop and the dog was baring her teeth as only a border collie can, all those rich upper teeth white shining.

'MacPherson, Rhoda MacPherson.' He had to shout because the dog was barking.

'Get out of this house,' my mother shouted.

'You must know more than any one else that there is a law,' he was shouting.

And my mother shouting back at him, 'King Herod made a law and it would be brains like yours addled by cowardice that would kill an infant.'

My mother never short of words knowing how to reinforce a sentence and all the time our dog moving slowly towards the detective and my mother not in the slightest way calling Jesse to heel, so that it was him who retreated back, moving beyond the closing door.

'You're a respectable person,' he was shouting through the letter box.

'You're an idiot and you know that you are abusing your authority.'

Mother shouted back and then our dog leapt at the letterbox, her lips pulled back over her teeth and it was over, the interview was terminated and Mother moved us all into the kitchen and reaching up onto the top shelf she found the tin box of dog biscuits and dipped them singly into Mr Morgan's honey and our dog Jesse wagging her tail looked at my mother in anticipation and I knew then for sure Jesse would have ripped out the man's throat had he not backed away.

It was a pleasant thought and comforted me immensely.

Next day it rained and all the burnt out debris in the saw mill percolated down into the ditches and into the drains so that dark grey leachings from the sawmill's foundations oozed out into the gutters each side of the road.

It was as if someone had lanced a giant boil and our house had become surrounded in black pus.

We had to jump over that black gutter when we went down to the station to see Rhoda off on her train. My mother pushing the pram, my sister sleeping inside and the dog walking ahead, leading ...

Like my dog does now when I take her for a walk, always looking back for the master, just to make sure I'm there walking, a true three point border collie out for a walk. And now I suppose somewhere perhaps Rhoda and Giuseppe live on ... but more likely they are dead, them being about the same age as my mother and father. But certain buildings in my town still hide their story and many more like them because buildings hold the stories of people and all their follies, and as I drive through my town picking up fares I sometimes catch the glimpse of certain characters, materialised images, ghosts trapped on street corners, a legend in my head, an out of focus aura, a very vague face, fading stories waiting to be told, to be remembered before they turn into empty spaces.

My town slowly turning into a dead town
with preservation order
a death warrant
hanging over its head.

# 11    *First Left and into Eternity*

It was half term and Big Bill Hogan and my father
were about to start looking for a gas leak on
Dinham Hill. Someone had phoned into the gas
works and reported that there was a smell of gas just
around the castle.

'It is a reasonable fact that this leak has been leaking all week,' said Bill to no one in particular, 'it's
just that someone of middle class origin with a telephone and more than enough influence in the ways
and means of things has smelt gas ... Ah, and it is a
great pity that there is not the scented gas, those
rumours that have been put about, much more of
that and someone will get the sack, or worse,
because if it were true and we had that kind'a thing
then we would be in the right direction, not that it
would matter a tinker's cuss.'

I could see that Bill was having a struggle with the
'road up' sign

'This thing is more than enough ...'

'I'll give yer a hand with that in a minute,'
shouted my Dad. And he said to me: 'Hold that sign
for Bill and make yourself useful.'

And so I held the sign that said 'ROAD UP' in
capital letters, each character painted red with half
a dozen small glass beads bedded into it. Each bead
about the size of a marble, a reflecting sign, with

cat's eyes. I held it up as Bill pushed the square arms into the square holes so that the sign stood in front of where Dad thought the leak was.

'Did yer read about it in the papers, Jack?'

'What's that, Bill?'

And Dad was hitting a small thin bar into the road surface and then he would pull it out and kneel down and smell the hole. He had made a line of holes starting from the top of the hill. They were now halfway down the hill.

Bill was a great reader, he used to take the *Daily Express* and the *Daily Herald*. 'Yer have ta ave both sides of the coin,' he would say. He would talk continually about one thing or another. Bill always wore a flat cap, he was never without it. He was a keep fit maniac. If he wasn't working then he would be stretching his arms into the air. He had great strong arms with huge muscles, he moved about with enormous strides. No matter what he said there was always a rhythm in his speech. He was never silent, 'What-der-yer-think-of-that', he would say and Dad would always say, 'That's right, Bill', or 'I-duna-know-about-that-Bill' according to whether a negative or positive response was required. Sometimes Dad would make a mistake and the Bill would say, 'What was that yer said?' but it did not matter because by then he was into another train of thought. And so it was that day when I held the sign up he started to talk about heavy water.

'It's one fine thing, that heavy water, Jack. I was readin' about it in the papers. Oh, and mind you the German has a brain that is so interesting because of the influence of the Jew, and all that, them having brains to invent all sorts of things. Jesus, the Jewish race is like an intellectual river.'

'What on earth are you talking about, Bill?'

'They probably boil it, Jack. They must have to do that in order to thin the water so that they can convert it into something else, washing off the surplus molecules, thereby making each molecule more pure than it was before and then compressing them, yes, that might make it heavy and then that would be it, the cooling of the heavy water, perfect for the manufacture of the atomic bomb.'

And all the time Dad was knocking his thin bar into the road and kneeling and smelling each hole so that he could locate the leak.

'I think it might be here,' he shouted to Bill. 'It will be where the main branches off into Camp Lane, it's halfway up the hill and the movement of the earth will have caused a fracture.'

'You could be right, Jack. Would yer like me to start the hole?'

'We can wait until the jack hammer comes, if yer like',

'Ah, whilst we are waiting I might as well remove the tarmac, the top layer will peel away like the skin of an apple ...'

But before he started Bill was finishing a sentence started five minutes or perhaps a week ago, 'there were some of them that seized avidly on that assumption but there were others that were divided in the interpretation of the knowledge'.

'Peel it away Bill', Dad said laughing to himself. And I felt the weight of my Dad's arm on my shoulder and I looked up at him and he whispered to me that Bill had swallowed so many words that he was overflowing and that the pity of it was that if only he could get them into some kind of order then it might make sense.

And so Bill Hogan started to dig a hole raising his pick into the air and making holes like perforations

on a postage stamp so that before my Dad had finished his cigarette the tarmac was lifted and the
stone hardcore was all laid bare, and then Bill
removed his shirt so that you could see his white
vest and all his muscles turned into knots as that
pick hit into those stones and then he ripped apart
the hardcore with the pick; it all looked so easy ...

'Will yer pass me them forceps, Jack'.

And my Dad was searching for the shovel that was
shaped like a heart, Bill's own shovel, a shovel all
polished like stainless steel.

Bill Hogan was surgical in the operation of his
shovel, the way he pushed it into the loosened
stones so that in no time at all he was standing knee
deep in his hole, it was as if he was a surgeon, cutting into the skin of the Earth. He cleaned the side
of the hole as he dug so that beneath the hard core
where the earth was clay it was smooth and as he
dug he placed the hard core in a separate pile from
the clay so that when the hole was back filled it
could be used again and all the time Bill talking
about one thing or another:

'Water, Jack ... I hate water, that's why I like working on the gas, tis a fact that there is no water. If
t'was a water main that we were looking for then we
would be up to our neck in shit, like a pair of bog
trotters we would be. Oh Jack I can remember the
peat bogs and the rain in angry drops dropping and
all the sky was grey and stormy with ducks labouring
across the wind and my father and I labouring up to
our knees in shit and that rain Jack was wet, it being
carried by an ill tempered wind.'

'Was it the heavy water, Bill?' said Dad.

'That water was as heavy as the heavy water, so it
was, ah ... and let me tell you that if them Germans
were to collect that water then it would do them fer

whatever they wanted to do with it, it was … Yes … so that in that bog we were trapped in a place where the four winds did meet and up on the mountain the rocks would gleam coldly at yer eye so that at night there was no heat in a peat fire, at all, at all, at all … and my poor mother God rest her soul … would be carrying water in from the outside so that we were forever careful with the water. And let me tell yer this Jack we were forever wearing sacks across our shoulders, head down through the sharp winds that were forever racing across the land'.

'It is not a green and pleasant land then, Bill,' my Dad said.

'No, Jack, tis a shite hole full of ignorance where even full grown men are shite scared of the priest and so we all came to Liverpool where there is more chance of the work …'

And then Bill paused from his shovelling and pulled out of his right hand pocket a red handkerchief covered in white spots and then he lifted his cap and wiped his head …

'Sweating is a very good thing for the health, you know, Jack. Ah, yes, I once knew this physician, who was a Harley Street man, and he said that sweatin' was the finest thing in the world for getting the toxins out of the system. That's what he called the shite that fouls up yer body and so I'm pleased to say that I sweat in a profuse manner. In fact you'll notice that a man given over to fat is not a man who sweats and the face of a fat man after any exertion is always red and gross as if gallons of thick blood have be pumped into it. And you'll see that the cheeks will be all bulging out with straggling purple veins and the pores of his skin will be inflamed owing to the blockage of the skin ducts altogether a sorry state

145

that man will be and incapable of any useful work altogether …

'Now then, Jack, what I'm thinking is this … and that what I think is that this ere main is nearer to us than we think because I am now looking at clinker which means that the main is probably beneath a layer of clinker … will yer pass Gregory, Jack, I'll loosen it, so I will.'

And Dad passed Bill's pick to him, it was his own pick, his personal pick, it was sharp and clean. Everything that Bill Hogan used was clean, even the long crow bar was clean, it looked chromed and no one ever touched any of Bill's tools, once Dad told me about one of the other labourers who picked up Bill's shovel and Bill shouted to him:

'HAVE YER GOT DENTURES?'

'No,' was the reply.

'YER WILL HAVE TA SEE PHIL TRANTER FER A SET IF YOO DON'T PUT THAT SHOVEL BACK FROM WHERE YOO HAVE FOUND IT … AND YOU WILL PUT IT DOWN GENTLY LIKE …'

It was that time when they were advertising in the paper for workers to build an aircraft factory in Gloucester, the footnote on that advert said 'Irish men need not apply'.

After Bill had read that advert he was running about like a mad bear. It was not the time to touch his shovel.

'Be Jesus, Jack, it's damp around this er clinker, der's a stream a run-in.'

'Dunna worry about it, Bill', Dad said. 'It'll follow its own course, anyway the thing of it is that even if there is a spring then it'll run downhill towards the river.'

Dad and I were watching Bill scratting away at the black cinder, he wore great hobnailed army boots that left nail patterns wherever he stood and his cord trousers were lifted just below his knee with 'Yorks' that looked like brown dog collars.

'Have yer still the tobacco plants, Jack?' Bill asked.

'This year I got the top patch full of Havana plants. I've found another way to make green cigars.'

'Is that a fact now, Jack?'

'And what's more I have bought some medium sweet cider. It runs more easily down the throat.'

'That is good thinking, Jack. By God, I could sink a few of them cow's horns right now, and in the name of the blessed Virgin Mary, it is a fact that that great liquid tasted better in them little horns than in the glass … Oh yes!'

And then the recollection of that evening seemed to give Bill a pretext, a cause to make intricate drinking gesturing with his great hands.

And I remembered the last time when Bill came to collect a few cabbage plants and he was holding the cow's horn in his great fist, like a small thimble it looked, and he was throwing the cider down his throat so that he lost count of the amount and then Dick Williams came from next door and there were three of them drinking because it was a hot evening and they had no money to go to the pub so they sat on the old pig-killing bench smoking Dad's green cigars and Dad was shouting:

'THE GREAT THING ABOUT IT IS THAT WE DO NOT HAVE TO PAY TAX ON ANY OF IT!'

And because of that fact, they really got stuck into the cider and then Bill let go the biggest fart that I have ever heard in my life, it was just like the kind of fart that Ted the old horse would sometimes let go and then would run around the field with his tail in the air trying to see where the fart had come from. But Bill never moved, instead he just said:

'I been waiting to let that go for a long time.'

'Jesus, Bill,' Dad said, 'something must ave crawled up your arse and died.'

And then they all started to laugh together and I saw the cotton that Dick Williams used to put in his ears so that he could sleep in the afternoon start to come out and then Dad and Bill were laughing at Dick who was the head postman and wore a uniform different to the other postmen and Dick pulled his forgotten cotton balls right out of his ears and then they all laughed together and then Dad got another quart from the refrigerator and explained that the cider was cooled by a flame and so they all started to laugh again, and then they were talking about Gerald Portlock's circus and how he had got a lion in a cage and then they were talking about his daughters who used to ride bareback round the circus ring and how their titties used to bounce and then they were laughing again and Bill wanted to piss and so Dad told him to do it against the hedge and that was how I saw Bill's tool and I saw that it was like a horse's tool except that it had a purple head and then they were all peeing in the hedge and then my mother called me and I had to go to bed and so left the three of them smoking green cigars whilst they drank cider, laughing at each other. It was past midnight when they came down the garden in the dark where there were steps.

Dad told them to hang onto the clothes line and so they all hung together and fell together and grazed their arms together and they all went to Dick's next door to try his bottle of Johnny Walker because they were afraid of getting lockjaw.

And the recollection of that evening made Bill stand upright in his hole and he said:

'That was some crack, that was, in the name of the blessed Virgin Mary, that was lethal, that stuff was'. And then Bill pointed towards the centre of his hole: 'The main, Jack,' he said, 'I've uncovered the main.'

Now what Bill had to do next was to uncover right around the gas main because the part that had fractured had to be cut out and to do this Dad would drill a hole each side of the fracture and then he would push what he called a pig's bladder into each hole and then blow the bladder up with a bicycle pump. The bladder would expand inside the pipe and stop the gas flowing. Before he did that he would connect a smaller gas main that would bypass the part that would have to be cut out.

My Dad liked to work with plenty of room, he liked to have as big a hole as possible. He liked to work with Bill because Bill would always dig a hole with plenty of room to work whereas the younger labourers would try to get away with a small hole. Dad could not stand a small hole. The trouble was that the hole would fill with live gas and then Dad and Bill would inhale the gas, that was why they always had a bottle of pop when they worked on a broken main. They would drink it and then belch and fart and so bring up the gas that they might have ingested.

'There is a great hog's head down here,' Bill shouted.

'You'd best scrat around with that pick that does not make sparks, Bill.'

'I'll not make a spark, it's gentle hitting that I'm doin ... let me ask yer something, Jack, I have

149

trouble with the club root now and I have no idea how it is that I'm goin' to be rid of it.'

'Ah, now then, Bill, I have got club root under control at that garden what I have in Galdeford. The thing is to double dig it and trench in some rhubarb leaves. Rhubarb is poisonous to three things, man beast and club-root.'

'Is that a fact, Jack?'

'What's more, the same can be said of spinach. The old leaves are poisonous, oxalic acid, Bill, just like rhubarb, same acid same use, kills club root.'

'Scalpel.'

And then Dad walked over to the wooden cart with all the tools and pulled out Bill's great silver crowbar, and Bill spat on his hands before he took it from my Dad.

'It's a great big hog's head you got there, Bill,' Dad said.

'He won't be there lon ...'

But before Bill could get the 'g' out of his mouth there was a huge explosion and then a great ball of flame and then all that my Dad and I could see was the figure of Bill Hogan struggling to escape from his hole and then as the keen heat from the fireball struck me in the face I felt myself being lifted by the scruff of my neck as my Dad gathered me up and threw me against the old town wall and then I saw it all anchored in my brain in slow motion: my Dad jumping across that hole, the explosion still ringing in my ears, him falling on top of Bill, both of them rolling down Dinham bank, the flames leaping up Bill's trouserleg and then my Dad rising to his feet and removing his jacket before he started to beat the great hulk that was Bill who was rolling over and over, capless, his silver hair burning and then my Dad throwing his jacket over Bill's head so that he was shouting muffled sounds and my Dad was thrown around like a bronco rider.

You could not imagine what my eyes were seeing, the gas main now turned into a great Bunsen Burner, a flame roaring up into the sky, up into the great yew hedge that hung over the town wall, that hedge spitting and moaning as the yellow flame licked into it. It was better than Guy Fawkes Day. It was better than the day the Americans let loose a flame-thrower in the park, it was supernatural and I was afraid so I ran to where my Dad was and saw him lifting his jacket off Bill's head and Bill sitting there quietly like a donkey examining the morning, bit by bit, his head moving slowly from side to side.

'In the name of the Blessed Virgin Mary, I thought that I had taken a left turn into eternity'. And Bill shook his head, his white hair now all yellow and singed. 'Me cap,' he said, 'me cap.'

'Burnt to a cinder,' Dad said, and Bill combed his fingers through his hair and then smelt his hand.

Meanwhile the yew hedge had stopped burning and was all red and glowing but the Bunsen Burner was still active and roaring like a great geyser and I had no idea what would happen next, and then my Dad looked as if he understood completely this unexpected happening.

'BACK FILL IT,' Dad shouted. 'BACK FILL THE HOLE'

And then Bill was fishing around in his trouser pocket until he pulled out his big red white-spotted handkerchief. He then tied each corner into a knot and placed it on his head.

'I cannot work wid me head uncovered,' he said.

And then Bill and my Dad grabbed shovels and started to back fill the hole, throwing in the clay first. They both worked fast in an almost supernatural harmony, the whiteness of my Dad's shirt becoming grey as it became wet with sweat, both men toiling together, bit by bit unhurryingly, each shovelful smothering the great flame until it became a diverse collection of burnings that danced around each shovelful like will-o-the-wisps.

I looked at them both walking over the hole where there were once flames, my thoughts still entangled in what I'd seen.

'Thank God fer me Yorks,' Bill was saying.

'What der yer mean?' said Dad.

'Had I not been wearing me Yorks, then God in heaven only knows what would have happened to me bollocks, that jet of flame leaping up me trouser leg would have made the whole affair into a major matter, me knackers would have shrivelled up like burnt walnuts. Now that would be someting to take home to the wife, a pair of burnt bollocks. Oh she would have liked that.'

And then Bill farted, bending his legs a little as he released his gas.

'Now, it's a good job that you did not drop that a few moments ago, Bill,' my father said. 'First left and into eternity it would have been for all on us.'

# 12    *The First Time was the Best Time Ever*

My grandmother on my mother's side was always sick. She was a small woman with an iron will who was always in hospital with strange-sounding illnesses that were always about to be fatal. But because of her iron will she always pulled through. These illnesses had completely depleted my mother's family of any life savings that they had scraped together so that when the Labour Party came to power there was a rejoicing never seen before. It was as if the Messiah had finally arrived, it was the Second Coming, and since Jesus Christ himself was the first Socialist, it was as if his disciples were themselves on the throne. And then just to prove that the system worked, my grandmother went down with gallstones.

In those days the only way to visit her was to take the bus. This was the period in our history when public transport was at its peak. The bus was cheaper than the train but took twice as long. It took two hours to travel the thirty miles to Shrewsbury and then another hour to catch a different bus for the five-mile journey to a place called Copthorne. Copthorne hospital was a collection of Nissen huts thrown together because of the war by the visually ignorant. Visiting hours were strictly

enforced, by the bell, two to a bed, so that you
waited until it was your turn and then you were
embarrassed when you had to kiss those thin blue
lips.

As soon as my mother sat down next to grandmother's bed, granny always found something for
her to do.

'Oh it's you Edna
make sure the flowers are put in water
by the way there's a sale at Hepworths
make sure you get your father a winter coat
check the price with the Fifty Shilling tailor's'
'I don't think there's one in Shrewsbury.'
'Well …'

And then she would pause and her claw-like hand
would reach out for a grape, and she would put it
into her mouth and she would chew but not swallow
the skin or the pips. My mother would place her
hand under her chin and the remains would dribble
out. It was thirty years before I could eat a grape.

'Well
check the price with …
there must be a Bon Marche
don't forget to air the spare bed
they might come up from Cinderford
oh oh yes …
the money for the rates is in the green jug.'

It amazed me, her concern about the rates. She
was in hospital and she was worrying about paying
the rates on time. She paid the rates the day they
were due. She was the first in the office under the
Town Hall. The whole family on my mother's side
had never been in debt, 'Out of debt out of danger'. You could nail that above their front door, and
to keep themselves out of debt they scrimped and
saved so that saving became part of their religion.

'You can have tea before you go back at Lyons, I hear they have one in Salop.'

It was marvellous how she knew about Joe Lyons' tea rooms, she was testing her daughter, but she had nothing to fear.

'I've got a flask,' my Mum said.

'Good ... see if the sale has started at Freeman Hardy & Willis,

did you use brown bread for the sandwiches?'

And then my mother would nod, 'Yes, mum.'

'Make sure they have plenty of roughage'. And she would look at my sister and I.

'Prevents cancer of the bowel later in life,' she would say and because she had spent more time in hospital than anyone else, she knew more about such things than anyone else.

Her obsession concerning regular motions bordered on the insane. When she came out of the hospital, it would start all over again, the same thing each day, my mother going up there on her bicycle just to make sure she passed a motion.

The great china bed pan removed from the commode and then lying down and the grunting and the screaming, it was like giving birth and then the great sigh of relief ...

'IS THERE MUCH?' she would shout.

That obsession was passed to my own mother who would ask us before we set out for the bus whether we had been or not and we were afraid to lie. We had to sit there until we had gone because we would be out all day. Six hours on the bus, four hours there, most of it spent waiting, ten hours altogether, soggy sandwiches, lukewarm tea. It was no wonder I wanted grandmother to die. It was no wonder that everybody was saving up for a car. But grandmother would not die, she had more than half her insides removed and she would not die and so we visited her every Sunday. It was worse than Sunday school.

Our family at that time was heavily involved in Local Government. Granddad was chairman of the Labour Party and believed that the world was flat. A proud man, he always walked with his head upright. He was famous for shouting:

ORDER, ORDER
THROUGH THE CHAIR
ORDER, ORDER

Dad was a Labour Councillor and was asked at a public meeting in the Town Hall who his employer was. It was a threat from Commander Pilling, a pillar of the church, and important enough for my father to let his feelings fly, knowing that since the gasworks was nationalised there was not much that Commander Pilling could do except ban him from the Hunt Ball. Mother loved that and prayed that the new Labour Government would ban fox hunting, so we left the Church of England and joined the Methodist Church.

It was the principle of the thing. Mother and father hated the way the big church worshipped the glory of war. At that time the Council always went to church on Sunday morning. It was a procession, the Mayor in his robes and the Councillors in their robes and the mace bearers, a tradition, Church and State and Sir Windsor Clive for ever, all democracy walking through our town, an example to be followed and then Dad and his friend Frank Acton decided that they would not worship in the big church, so they both walked to the great Norman door and then they turned round and they left the procession. They both walked down Broad Street to the Methodist church and the whole town watching those two men demanding the impossible, my Dad who had never been to war and Frank Acton who had a chest full of medals walking into the Methodist Church. Ten minutes later the whole congregation, heads bowed in prayer, brother Frank and brother Jack, and that was how my sister and I went to Sunday School in a plain floor-boarded room with seats that were purgatory.

That was how it was supposed to be. There was no enjoyment at all, you read from the Bible prompted by Mr Hammond, who had a club foot, starting with Genesis chapter one verse one to eight and so you learnt that God created Heaven and Earth in six days and that he rested on the seventh day and that we were all born in sin.

That was Sunday. During the week my father's evenings were spent writing letters. He was mad keen for our town to have a swimming pool. He had found that the Public Health Act of 1936 and the Physical Training Act of 1937 and the Local Education Authority Act of 1944 made it a duty under those acts that provision should be made for a swimming pool.

But it was an uphill battle.

Half the Council (the Tories), wanted to improve the banks of the river so that it would be safer to swim in the river for the two months of the year when it was warm enough because a swimming bath would never be a paying proposition and would be a drain on the rates and the other half (the Labour and independents), wanted a full size pool, they even wanted a diving board!

I was just twelve and a half and had a problem with my penis. It kept growing. That was important enough but I also knew that the world was round and that the moon had at one time been part of the Earth. The small bravery of knowledge gave me confidence to question the Bible and to dispute with Mr Hammond the fact that the world was created in seven days. It was important to me, so like my Dad, I let my feelings fly and was removed from the small dull room with the white clean floor boards to another chapel in another street, to where the big children worshipped. I went to Sunday school in the basement of a disused church in Old Street on my own, knowing that I would not be accepted by those who were three years older than me.

It was madness and terror knowing that I was growing into a man with the ticking in my balls, all wound up like a clock, and what was more, Mr Hammond's daughter was there and turning into a woman and had bosoms like Jane Russell ...

My first love, but she never knew and I had blackheads on my chin that went septic and then I had a great boil on the back of my neck and my nose went red.

Sad, sad, sad,

All my feelings boiling over until one Friday night I just could not stop soaping the end of my dick.

The first time was like the best feeling that I have ever experienced ... ever ... ever ... ever.

All my life standing there, me watching it afterwards shrink not understanding a thing about it at all, just that I knew that I would not be able to ignore it any more.

And all the time Miss Hammond growing into a woman with all the older boys smelling around her and me watching from the very peripherals of that room because even at the Christmas party I was not invited to play Postman's Knock. So cruel, me left out on the edge because I was three years younger and had blackheads. That was how I found my father's green cigars, that was how I learnt to smoke them, to smoke away the bad world and Miss Hammond's bosoms ... inside my Dad's shed and all those hanging tobacco leaves and his six gallons of cider cooling inside the giant gas fridge, and the heat from that stove with the tortoise on the front, the tooting of the tank engine from Tenbury as shovelfuls of coal rolled down the embankment ... and I did stack that coal well, it did look good beside the stove and I was very strong there in those shadows, that day when I told my Dad that I was not going to go to Sunday school any more ...

'Well,' he said, 'we'll see about that', and then he looked at me as if he knew more about me than I did.

'I'll see you after school in Frank Roberts' shop,' he said.

And that was how I came to try a spade for size. It was double digging with a spade that had a 'D' handle so that blisters would not form between my fingers and when I stood up to see how much we had done, Dad said;

'Yer back only aches when you straighten up. Keep yerself bent a little. We'll finish this patch and then we'll have a glass of cider'.

It was in many ways better than the Methodist Church Sunday School, that was up for sale, and was wanted by someone who was going to make trousers.

Bad memories, except for those bosoms thought about over and over again while digging so that Dad could plant peas and broad beans, and the taste of new potatoes, and soaring runner beans and seed beds, lettuce, radishes, carrots, onions and the early apples coming out sweet-tasting in the month of June.

Everything in the garden was lovely, I dug most of it, Dad planted it, and our family lived off it. And my Dad was always at Council meetings, so I never had to wait for him to go to the pub before I could smoke a green cigar and then I would sit on the old wooden bench and smoke away trying to eradicate those merciless swinging breasts that came to me in waves until I could stand it no more and spat into my hand, giving in to fishnet stockings and women stumbling on high heels, thinking that I was mad and sex crazy ...

Until it all became suddenly quiet and I shut the chickens up and the first light of evening began to dissolve the town and I stood there looking at the hills all purple and dark until I was embarrassed and it was cold, and I had not forgotten to clean and oil my spade nor to look up at the window that was the bedroom of the girl next door.

# 13 *Keysells*

If you walked from the Buttercross down the narrows, the shops started with Bodenhams gents and ladies outfitters. Opposite Leonards shoe shop, next to Bodenhams the dress shop where my mother did alterations, opposite that Voughts which was almost a department store where you could see pantyhoses, garter belts and long nylon stockings, the shop where they displayed the first bikini on a headless torso and we tried to imagine which girl would dare to wear it and debated what would happen to the top in the water if she did. The Bishop keeping his thoughts to himself suggested that it be displayed discreetly inside ... but it was too late, and my father's cousin who was a minister at the Congregational church preached a sermon, the whole theme of which was about temptation and we had to pray for a girl who had conceived out of wedlock.

'LET US PRAY FOR THOSE AMONGST US WHO HAVE SINNED.'

'AMEN,' someone shouted.

'THE LORD IS MERCIFUL,' shouted someone else.

And then we said the Lord's prayer and I wondered what a girl would do if she could be tempted to wear a bikini on a beach or even at Leominster swimming pool but Tony from next door who was two months older than me said that there was a notice up at Leominster swimming pool banning bikinis, 'One piece swimsuits only,' it said. I felt ashamed and really did ask the Lord to forgive me my trespasses ... because the girl who was going to have a baby could not have owned a bikini since the first one had only just arrived in our town ... lead us not into temptation ... the harder I prayed the more I thought about the girls in the top form who played netball and had titties and long legs, and then I could feel my willy getting hard and my cousin was looking at me, he who had just preached was looking directly at me and my dick was hard. I was in church and my dick was hard. I looked directly ahead into the twin shafts of sunlight that filtered into that church from the round window above the altar and I thought about the two or three cases of spontaneous combustion that happened throughout the world each year, those very rare cases when people just blew up without reason ... probably because they had hard dicks ... and God saw everything, especially hard dicks and the more I thought about getting a soft dick the harder it became.

That evening in the Congregational church I was trembling so much that I could hardly say 'Amen'.

Next Monday morning before the Bishop said prayers, a girl was sent home for wearing a 'T' shirt that was too tight.

'We are entering a decade of sin,' the Bishop said, but none of the boys in my class seemed to be afraid.

Next door to Vought's was The London Tea Company, where you could get breakfast teas, afternoon teas, Darjeeling teas, Ceylon teas, or China teas. Next door to that there was Wainwrights the tobacconist where you could buy green cigars that burned faster than the ones my Dad made. Opposite Wainwrights, the Maypole, where they still patted butter, Wap, Wap, Wap, tightly wrapped, and then there was Tay's the butchers, directly in front of Gaius Smith's, grocers, with branches in Clee Hill and Tenbury.

If you walked on towards the Bull Ring then you would have to pass Keysells and its twin multi-framed windows with a backing of black wire mesh and the legend 'KEYSELLS WINE VAULTS' written in gold leaf paint that was faded and cobwebbed, and there was a mechanical barometer that told whether the population was about to suffer from high or low pressure fronts.

Keysells was more an off licence than a pub. Just inside the door was a long low pewter-topped bar. At the end of this bar there was a gas flame burning continually on the end of a brass burner, it was blue flamed and was for the use of smokers. The wooden floors were scrubbed white, the walls were white, the ceiling was white. It was minimal decor, but in those days we had no idea what the word minimal-ism meant.

In the back room Mr Turpin did the accounts in longhand wearing a black cuff over his right hand. If you wanted to order drinks to be delivered to your home then you went into the back room and ordered them directly from Mr Turpin who would make a note of your needs.

Keysells were wine merchants. They imported wines and spirits, they were agents for Allsopp and Bass and Dublin stout in cask and bottle, and they had a bottling plant that bottled every drink they sold, and every bottle had the Keysell label.

'WHISKY BOTTLED BY KEYSELL & CO LUDLOW'

or

'GIN BOTTLED BY KEYSELL & CO LUDLOW'

There was no messing about with the labels, they said what was in the bottle. It was the same for every drink they sold, everything distributed and bottled in the town so that the customers knew exactly what they were getting.

'Send up two dozen bottles of Guinness and a bottle of gin. Oh, and you might as well send up a couple of bottles of port. How's Mrs ... ah.'

'Oh fine, yes she's much better now, thank you. How much do I owe you, Mr Turpin?'

'Now, let me see, that's ... um, let me see ... yes um ... ah here it is ... that'll be £4:8s:5d. The account is up to date as of this morning, by the way I have not charged on the bottles.'

'I tell you what, might I take one bottle of port with me just in case of an emergency?'

'By all means, but Tom will be up on Monday.'

'I'll take it with me.'

'As you wish.'

And Mr Turpin would come back with the bottle of port wrapped in brown paper.

There was always a fire in the back room. There was nothing exclusive about the room, but it was here that a certain group of customers drank. They had their own chairs and as they drank and then moved out, others came in to replace them so that as the room changed the more it remained the same. Bank Managers, schoolteachers, policemen out of uniform, tax officers, councillors, aldermen, and on occasion even the clergy, all these drank in the back room. Whilst in the big pewter bar were rat catchers, road sweepers, carpenters, bricklayers, labourers, painters, and on Saturday mornings a lady who could drink thirty-six bottles of stout without going to the toilet.

And now that grandmother had finally suffered and died from one of her serious illnesses, Granddad at last learnt to appreciate the taste of stout without sucking full strength peppermints. And what was more, he could drink in the back room and would not have to worry about anyone seeing him leaving by the front door, except the Baptist minister. But he still used the back door and looked up and down the street before he went in or out.

One Saturday morning I saw Granddad walking down towards Keysells' back door.

'I'm just going to Tays the butcher's,' he said.

But he knew and I knew that since my Dad's bike was outside then he was inside and we could hear sounds from inside which were clearly drinking sounds so Granddad said that it was a wonderful coincidence that my father was there as he had to see him about getting some sulphur to burn in his greenhouse, owing to the fact that he had a very bad case of mould and he thought that was the only way to get rid of it. He also asked me if I would like a bottle of pop, and he said that it would be all right if I stood in the back room since it was an office, and therefore technically unlicensed. He was so correct and law-abiding, was Granddad, he would never have let me go into any other pub except Keysells, but he had changed since grandmother died, and now he never bothered to suck mints.

And that was how I came to be standing between the fire and Mr Turpin's desk and saw the two men who had moved into the big house in Mill Street get into a passionate argument about the history of

English Literature and how the Americans were the only ones able to write a modern novel. And the one that was called 'Noel' got so upset that he started to slap the other one who upset his port and then started to apologise to Mr Turpin, so much so that Mr Turpin ended up apologising instead.

'Pataphysics,' said my father. 'That's the solution.'

And then Cocky Wontner who had just been to America for his two weeks' holiday said:

'Aaww,' he said, 'I've read every modern American book that there is,' he said, 'and if you con give me the names of any new uns then I'll order them from the Octagon Library'.

But when the men who wore large bow ties told Cocky about John Steinbeck and Ernest Hemingway, Cocky said:

'Naw,' he said, 'they ana wrote a good cowboy book between um.'

What the two men who had bought the big house did not know was that Cocky had never been to America in his life. He used to borrow a dozen cowboy books and then read them during his holiday without ever leaving his house, in fact it was rumoured that he used to have his wife feed him bacon and beans on an enamel plate, knocking before he would open the door. This was probably not true, but what *was* true was that before Cocky's holidays Jack Davis, manager of the Co-op, used to get two pounds of American blend coffee beans and roast them and grind them coarse so that they could be boiled in an enamel jug and then filtered and drunk without milk.

'Just like they have it out on the range,' Jack told my Dad.

But Dad did not take to coffee in the same way

that Cocky did, although he read almost as many cowboy books but over a year.

'I just can'a condense them into two weeks, like you do,' Dad said.

'Pity,' Cocky said. 'Completely immerses the brain, after the second day you never knows whether you are there or not, and after the end of the second week you might as well have been there because you'll know more about it than if you'da bin there, and you just ain't got the risk of all that travellin'.'

'But, how do you stand not going out of the house for two weeks?' Dad asked. Cocky had come over for a drink of cider and a green cigar the week before he went on his latest trip to the United States.

'You just takes the rough with the smooth,' Cocky said. 'Makes a break.'

So I knew more about my Dad and Cocky than the two men did who had paid £2000 for a house in Mill Street and had an Armstrong Siddeley motor car parked across the road and were surprised that they did not know about the science of Pataphysics.

'You see,' my Dad said, 'anything that you can imagine is always inferior to the magic of reality itself, in it, Cocky?'

And Cocky Wontner who had just been to America for two weeks nodded to my father and then he nodded to the two men in bow ties that he would accept a drink from them. It was then that Granddad managed to butt in to the conversation:

'Der you know anything about fumigating a greenhouse, John?' he asked.

He was the only one except my mother who called my Dad John and so Dad looked at Granddad the way he always did when he called him John, and remained silent until he spoke to the man who had started to slap the other man with the bow tie when they were arguing about literature.

'Do you as learned gentlemen know anything about fumigating a greenhouse?' Dad asked.

'No,' one said. 'We are literary agents.'

And then they both nodded together.

'Tweedle Dum and Tweedle Dee,' Cocky whispered. And that was how they got their names.

'The groaning ghost,' Granddad said. And I didn't know why it was that Granddad started to talk about the ghost in the castle.

And then the notary, who was always dressed in a pinstripe suit and a bowler hat and had snow white hair, the man you went to if you had to swear on oath, said, 'It's the hanging tower,' he said, 'that's where the groaning was heard.'

'But that was a long time ago,' Cocky said. 'It was in 1948, that was the last time it was heard.'

'Jim Stokes' dog came running from there uth his hairs standin' up like as if he'd been struck by lightning,' Bob Davis said, as he got up to go to the bar, 'hell of a thing, came from around that castle like a bolt from hell, that dog did'.

Bob Davis was an engine driver, he drove the Castle Class locomotives, he used to lodge in Shrewsbury, he was what I wanted to be, an engine driver, he was my hero, I believed everything he said.

'There was two boys that heard it first,' Cocky said, 'they was around by the old yew tree uth two wenches.'

'Wenchin',' Granddad said, and he shook his head from side to side.

'That must ave put the fear of God into em', Cocky said.

'The hanging tower ...'

But my Dad never finished because what Cocky did was to put his arms around Tweedle Dum and Tweedle Dee and he said to them very quietly, 'The drinks, I'll give you a hand to carry the drinks' and Cocky had the ability to make his eyes stand out so that they were well rounded and he held his right hand up with his first finger in the air, and Tweedle Dum and Tweedle Dee went out with Cocky to the room with the pewter bar, to where Tom Burton was serving and then after a pause Granddad said to Dad,

'Fumigation.'

'Ah', Dad said, 'Go down to Frank Roberts' and ask him for Roll Sulphur, but if he does not have any then flowers of sulphur will do, you'll need an ounce and you put it onto an old biscuit tin lid in the middle of the greenhouse, make sure that it is right bang in the middle and then light the sulphur and retire immediately, stand clear and close the door and make sure that the vent is closed, too. Look at it from outside and when you see's a blue flame then you'll know that the sulphur is burning properly. Do not go into the greenhouse because if you want a pair of tonsils like golf balls then that's what you will have if you breathe even a small amount of them fumes in. Leave it overnight, and you will find that the moulds have gone and all the insects are dead. In fact the greenhouse is dead. But what I do is to change the soil afterwards because it don't grow tack like it used to unless you change the soil.'

When Dad had finished telling Granddad how to fumigate his greenhouse Cocky came in holding a round tin tray full of drinks. There was even a bottle of pop for me.

Dad looked at Cocky and Cocky said, 'They gone fer wee wee'.

And then I saw that each drink had a small whisky glass beside it and then I knew that Cocky and Dad were going to have a session and I wondered whether Granddad would also have a session, and then I saw Bob Davis the engine driver reach over towards the tray and wink at Cocky who winked back and I saw that Bob Davis had in his trouser pocket a handful of rags just like an engine driver would have, but Bob was wearing cord trousers and not his blue overalls like he did when he was in his engine. It must be habit, I thought as I watched him clean his pipe out and then wipe the mouthpiece on the rags. They all sipped a little beer and then they followed those sips with gentle sips of whisky.

'Twelve so far, Jack', Bob Davis said to my Dad.

'Her's a third way there then,' said Dad to Cocky.

'Her must ave some tackle between her legs,' said Bob.

'I bet her plumbing flaps, I bet it makes a purrin' noise when her does go,' Cocky said and he started to laugh, and then they all started to laugh, even my Granddad was laughing and Mr Turpin was smiling and said:

'Last Saturday it was thirty-three. Tom puts the empty bottles under the counter'.

'Is that so then?' my Dad said. 'I reckon that her should pass thirty this week'.

'No, not this week,' Bob Davis said, 'It's too cold. You ever bin on a motor bike when it's cold an all you can do is pee? Too cold, her might have a job to go past twenty'.

'Thirty, I'll start at thirty, a shilling says that she passes thirty'.

Cocky was starting a sweepstake on the number

of bottles of Guinness the lady sitting at the pewter bar would drink before she had to go to the toilet.

They all loved having a sweepstake on one thing or another. Once they had had a sweepstake on how fast Paddy Reynolds could drink a pint of beer. He had the knack of being able to hold his clack back so that the beer would disappear down his throat fast, he would pour it down and you could hear it running into his tummy like water running into a barrel from a hose. He could drink a pint in six seconds. But the important thing when betting was to bet safely. So it was imperative that you had someone who did not know that it was possible to drink a pint in six seconds or how it was done, then you could really up the stakes.

Once I saw Cyril Bursnell eat a frog, it was only a baby frog and he put it on his tongue and Cyril touched its back legs and it jumped down his throat. There was five pounds made on that bet not counting the beer that the Birmingham fishermen had to buy. And then there was the young ginger-headed Welshman who would eat a glass for a pound. It used to take him all evening, he would bite the rim and then he would slowly chew the glass into dust and swallow it down with deep drafts of beer. It would take him all evening but he'd eat a glass, and he would drink eight pints and still go home with a pound.

They were always at it. Phil Tranter who was a dental technician used to put a single false tooth into a glass of beer and then he would ask the barman if he had lost a tooth when he'd got to the bottom of the pint, of course he had another free pint. Sometimes things would go wrong like the time when Phil pulled the same stroke on the barmaid with the big breasts, who had only just started at

The Blue Pig and she went all red-faced, and every one in the bar was laughing at her, and Phil with his pocket full of teeth, but the next night Phil found a tooth in his glass that was small with a hole, a child's tooth. 'What the hell,' he shouted when he saw it. 'The tooth fairy must have dropped it,' said the barmaid with the bosoms.

'By God, Dicky, you should have seen her jubbies heaving when she laughed,' said Dad as he told it to Dicky in the shed and then they both laughed, and Dicky said that he might have to try one in the Blue Pig.

They were always going into a pub to try one, it was as if they were beer inspectors, and how they all laughed when they had caught somebody out and if it was somebody from away they all laughed harder. That was how I knew that Cocky was about to catch the two men who had bought the big house in Mill Street.

'It's a private matter,' he said when Tweedle Dee and Tweedle Dum asked what was going on.

'There's been a ghost in the castle since the time that Henry Two was on the throne,' Dad said, 'and that was eleven twenty-six.'

My Dad was good at dates, he could bang a date out so that you really believed that it was the correct date. We were up in the shed once and I asked him how it was that he knew so many dates, 'I don't,' he said, 'what you have to do is to get it thereabouts and then make the statement in such a way that it sounds correct, no one ever checks a date unless they got a book and no one ever has a book handy so you can in general make up any date that you see fit.' And it worked.

'Let um in on it,' said Bob Davis.

'On what?' said the notary, who had been reading his copy of the *Telegraph*.

'No, no,' said Cocky. 'It's a very private matter, a delicate subject, concerning the amount a certain woman can hold in her bladder without having to pass the said ...'

'Cocky,' Granddad said.

'What it is,' said Bob Davis, 'is that there is a woman in the bar who drinks every Saturday up to thirty bottles of stout without passing her water.'

'Impossible,' said the notary. 'The size of the bladder is insufficient'. And the notary said it with the conviction of a man who has to spend his time witnessing people swearing on oath.

'Ah, but ... but ... but ... and but again', and you could see that there were little devils in Cocky's eyes, 'I am going to bet that she will pass the thirty-sixth bottle today ... without passing so much as a teardrop from her plumbing.'

'Cocky,' shouted Granddad. and Tweedle Dum and Tweedle Dee the literary agents were nudging each other and the notary was shaking his head, and I saw that there were flakes of dandruff on the notary's shoulders, and then Mr Turpin was looking over his horn-rimmed glasses.

'Not even a tear drop, and I will have a pound note on it at five to one,' and everybody looked at Cocky.

And then the notary said, looking over his newspaper, that it was just not possible, that the bladder was not big enough, 'but I'll put a pound on it that she will not go more than twenty half pint bottles,' he said.

'We are rolling, we are rolling', and Cocky was singing and that was how it was that the whole back room bar were betting on the amount of bottles that the woman who drank stout could drink without having to go to the toilet, and Cocky was explaining to the literary agents that there was only one toilet and that she would have to pass through the back room to use it and that if she left before she arrived at the lowest bet, which was the notary's bet and he was the next best thing to a solicitor he said, then all monies would be returned and that she was already on bottle number twelve, so that there were only eight to go, and it must have tickled the fancy of the two literary agents Tweedle Dum and Tweedle Dee because they put five pounds on bottle twenty-two, and then Granddad put ten shillings on twenty-seven.

'Thirty-six,' Dad said, 'ten shillings on thirty-six.'

'We are rolling', Cocky kept on singing and then they had to wait. And for a few moments there was a silence until Cocky told the two literary agents that my Dad used to play dominoes with the Emperor Haile Selassie, the King of Ethiopia. They were so interested and happy when they learned that the King was exiled in our town that they wanted to buy Dad a drink, and so Cocky had to take the tray back to have it filled and each time he took the tray back he reported on how many bottles the lady had drunk, and when it passed twenty the notary was so angry that he rolled the *Daily Telegraph* up into a ball and said that he just did not believe it.

'Believe it or not, one pound if you please,' Cocky said.

But he would not pay up until the lady reached twenty-two. After she passed that number and he had paid Cocky, he stood up and finished his sixth glass of port, he then removed his bicycle clips from his left pocket, bent down, clipped his trousers, stepped over to the peg that held his hat, almost bowed as he headed outside for the toilet, turning just as he passed through the door so that he might smile at Mr Turpin who had raised his hand.

As Mr Turpin lowered his hand Tweedle Dum and Tweedle Dee got extremely excited, especially when Cocky told them that she had slowed up, they were so excited that they sent Cocky back for another round even though the current round was not yet finished, so that I had already drank four bottles of pop and wanted to pee but crossed my legs because I was afraid to go until someone I knew went, because I was not sure how I would be able to get back in and Granddad kept removing his trilby hat and wiping the inside rim with his white hand-kerchief each time he chased his stout down with a sip of whisky.

It was very hot in the back room and the woman was still on twenty-two and had slowed up. I could not hold it any longer, and so I followed Granddad into the urinal and peed holding my right hand over my penis just like all the older men did, and Granddad said that he was very pleased that I knew how to pee, and that he was going to buy a TV. I was dumfounded especially since he had told me that he was going to buy a television in the urinal at the back of Keysells.

'It's the cricket,' he said, 'I wants to watch the cricket.'

Before I could digest what Granddad had said Cocky came in to the urinal and asked me how I was getting on with my running. He kept talking to me about Emil Zatopek who was the greatest run-ner in the world and my hero, but when Granddad went out before me, Cocky pulled me to one side and asked me if I could keep a secret and would I like to earn half a crown. What I had to do was to go down to the empty crates and take five empty bottles of Guinness out of the crates that were stacked up for return and run them round the front pewter bar and give them to Tom Burton, which meant that I had to go all around the block and back again, because I had to come in through the back room. I was not to go through the bar. Cocky gave me a real half crown and when he put it into my hand I had to swear that I would not look at it or take it out of my pocket until I got home. I had to swear with it in my hand when Cocky's hands were wrapped around mine and I had to swear on my mother's life that I would do as Cocky told me.

When I got back into Keysells back room the woman had got to twenty-five and I saw Cocky taking a five pound note from the hand of Tweedle Dee. Granddad was very excited and bought a round. It was the first time that Granddad had ever been known to buy a round, and Dad said that they should hoist a flag up on the Butter Cross. But Granddad laughed and sipped his stout. I wanted to tell Dad that Granddad was going to buy a television but the Tweedle Dum and Tweedle Dee were asking Dad about Emperor Haile Selassie and his big bodyguards, who were supposed to be eunuchs, so it was not possible to tell him that Granddad was going to buy a television.

By the time the clock in the back room had got around to twenty-five past two the lady in the pewter bar had gathered up her cigarettes, together with her Ronson lighter, into her black handbag and then she walked through the door and into the back room. It was very silent as she walked towards the door that lead to the single upstairs toilet that only women used and I saw that she wore high heels like the ones Mrs Williams wore when she went out to the pub and that as she lifted them from step to step her feet made half circles.

As she closed the door Tom Burton came into the back room and shouted across to Cocky:

'Thirty-five,' he said, 'thirty-five it is.'

The white five pound note looked strange on the little table, it was more than my Dad earned in a week and there were three other pound notes and Granddad's ten shilling note. Cocky looked gleefully at all that money. He rubbed his hands together and he scratched his head and as he picked up those notes he turned them so that they were all the correct way up. And then the men who were literary agents and wore bow ties shook Cocky's hand and said that they had never had so much fun in their lives.

I was afraid to move and stood still watching Cocky folding the notes into his top pocket. It seemed like a fortune and his enormous delight opened my eyes and I saw a picture of myself walking into Larkham's toy shop and paying for a Hornby train, a Double OO electric train, and walking home with it under my arm.

When the woman came back into the room I saw that she looked younger than my mother but she had deep crow's feet each side of her eyes and there were deep lines around her lips, lips that were red. When she had gone out and into that Saturday afternoon Bob Davis said:

'Her works in Tenbury, in Richard Lloyds. Her husband was in the K.S.L.I., he had his face shot completely away, lived fer six months without a face, her mon did.'

And then there was a very long silence punctuated by Tom Burton bottling up in the pewter bar.

'Come on,' Granddad said suddenly, and he took

me by the hand. It was three o'clock, Saturday after-noon, the chimes from St Laurence's Church echoed along the narrows. And then we saw the preacher standing in front of the Buttercross. It was as if he was submerged up to his armpits in the thick blackness of his bible. Next to him a man carried a giant drum on his belly. He was a little excited, but all the time he smiled. And then the preacher's body tensed, and because it was warm and he had on a Salvation Army uniform there was perspiration gathering on his bald scarred head. I wanted to stop, I wanted to turn back, but Granddad held my hand tight. Legend had it that the preacher's skull was made from a silver plate, he had had his head kicked in … brained by a horse. His forehead was all furrowed. He knew Granddad, he knew me. He knew that we had been in Keysells, that we had all been betting, that we had sinned. He knew.

All of a sudden his face contracted with effort, his eyes bored into us, his body lifted and his arms were raised. Then suddenly from his lips there exploded verses from the Old Testament:

'IF A MAN SHALL STEAL AN OX, OR A SHEEP
AND KILL IT, OR SELL IT
HE SHALL RESTORE FIVE OXEN
FOR AN OX
AND FOUR SHEEP FOR A SHEEP'

And people moved away from the preacher and they looked at each other and they exchanged glimmers of smiles that were faint smiles of embarrassment, and then they moved, dissolving into the crowd without face or individuality.

I lowered my head and ducked as I passed the preacher.

# 14  *Granddad*

My Granddad was a baker, he made the best-tasting bread in our town. Of course, that was before there was sliced bread, before we lost one of our primary tastes, when there were a dozen bakers in our town, when there were bakers in little streets like Bell Lane, when there was fresh bread on the table every day because you could buy it from the baker up the road, just like they still do in France.

My Granddad could also make cakes and pastry. He once made a wedding cake that was taller than I was and he taught me how to make pastry. I wanted him to teach me how to make the Christmas Log or the six-layered sponge cake, with layers of jam and buttercream but he said that I would have to learn how to make basic dough first, that I would have to learn the technique. He said that the simplest things were the most difficult and that once you had learnt the basic technique of doing things then the rest would follow.

I was eleven when he taught me how to make pie dough. It was October and we had hundreds of Genet Moyle apples. The Genet Moyle apple is a cooker, an eater and a keeper. It is the oldest apple in the world, it came from France, it was brought to England by my great great great granddad.

When we picked the apples, those without any

blemishes were wrapped in newspaper and were laid out under every bed in the house so that we slept with the scent of apples from the end of October until Easter.

The apples with the blemishes were made into chutneys or apple jam. Most of the pantries down our street were full of jams and chutneys The chutneys were always stored in stone jars, the jams in jam jars, that was how it was. If your pantry wasn't full then there was something up because no one bought jams or chutneys or even cakes, everything was homemade, you never knew what kind of chemical they put into shop jam.

Dad said that shop stuff was preserved, whereas home cured stuff was matured.

It was the last week of summertime, a Saturday, when Granddad taught me how to make pie dough:

2 cups of flour

6 ounces of sweet butter cut into small cubes

1/4 teaspoon of salt

1/2 teaspoon of sugar

1/3 of a cup of water

The best part was when I put all those things into the brown stone bowl and mixed them all together with my fingers. The feel of the butter squeezing, the touch of the sugar and the salt dissolving, the flour coating, and then the water added, and then the start of the kneading and all the time my Granddad talking:

'Do not worry if there are little pieces of butter here and there, it'll make the dough flaky, and that's nice. Make it malleable.'

'What's malleable, Granddad?'

'So's it'll work, like, but don't over work it. I don't want it like elastic.'

And it was harder to do all those things than you

would think, it seemed to me that everything I was doing was wrong and if he had not been giving a running commentary to what I was doing then everything would have been even more wrong:

'Remember that the more you knead it
and the more water you use the more it will shrink
and become like elastic
the less water and the more fat you use
the more crumbly the dough will become
let me tell you that there are three main doughs:
bread dough, which is flour and water
and then at the other end
cake dough, flour and fat,
this dough is in the middle
you've got enough water
do not use any more water
now then when you can make a ball
then you have it about right
when it stops sticking
that's when you got it about right
but it will always stick
that's why we're gonna put flour on the board
when we do roll it'.

And all the time he was talking his breath was rolling over my head and there was a certain fragrance to his breath that was different to my father's ...

'Now then spread a little flour on the board
a little more
that's enough
and now keep turning the dough as you roll it
like a wheel
always turning it the same way
making a wheel
m a k i n g   a   w h e e l

and you want it about 1/4 of an inch thick
but you can have it thinner
some like it thinner
I like it thicker
gives a base to the tart
so's that you can hold it
when you puts it up to yer mouth without breaking
that's it
now it's round.

'Now what I'm going to do next is to roll the dough back onto the rolling pin so that I can put it onto the pie dish, and I want you to watch this because you are going to do it just as I have done it but first you are going to learn how to put it on the rolling pin'.

And that was how I learnt how to take rolled out dough from the dusted board and how to roll it back out across a pie dish and how with the tips of my fingers I pushed the corners of the dough into the bottom edge of the pan, a well buttered pan, and then I had to squeeze a lip all around the inside of that pan, working the dough between my thumb and finger, and then when it was done as it should be done I was told to roll the rolling pin over the pie dish pressing down with all my weight, and it was like magic when I saw the sides of that pie dish appear, and then I had to watch Granddad re-form the edge of the dough, to lift it up a little, and then to make crimping edges with the tines of a fork.

He did half of the pie and I did the other half and all the time he was talking so that when I'd fin-ished you could not tell who had done what part of the pie.

Next the apples, our apples, and after Granddad

had peeled the apples and removed the cores he cut them in half and then he showed me how to slice them with his knife.

His knife was the sharpest knife that there was and he showed me how to hold it so that the blade was sliding up and down the middle part of my fingers ... but I could not do it, not that day, not like Granddad did, he was so fast that the knife seemed like a blur, instead I arranged all the chopped apples along the bottom of the pie and then he showed me how to fan out the slices one by one, and because the pie was a special pie for my mother, his daughter, Na No, he made the centre like a rose.

And then Granddad placed the pie in his oven and I had to wait for one hour and ten minutes and whilst I waited he made me hold his spatula across my fingers, like as if it was a knife and practise cutting and all the time I was practising he was telling me that I was not holding it correctly so that I got angry and I almost spoilt that morning until he told me that he wanted apple jam sieved and diluted with a little water so that we could glaze the tart when it came out of the oven.

I was eleven when I made my first apple tart.

I was twelve when Granddad retired.

Six months after Granddad retired he started to work part time for Mr Flemmings.

Mr Flemmings was a wholesale herbalist. He had a warehouse down Portcullis Lane. It was a square black clapboard building with a roof like I thought a Chinese pagoda would look like. It was always shrouded in brown dust. My grandfather went from the white dust of flour to the brown dust of dried herbs.

When he used to call me into the bakehouse to

have my fresh baked cob, he would brush away the white dust from his trousers. When he was at Mr Flemmings it was a dried herb dust. When we went to see him with my mother, he would shout 'Na No!' That was my mother's nickname before she was married.

And how's my Na No? he would say. It was the remains of my mother's first life and she would worry about him and the dust and he would lift my sister and I and hug us so that we could see our reflection in his glasses, and then we would blow the dust from his eyebrows, he had eyebrows like giant moustaches almost meeting over the bridge of his great nose.

'Now, Na No,' he would say, 'how far have you got?'

And that day my mother said, 'Forget-me-nots.'

'Myosotis,' he said.

'Myosotis scorpioides, the water forget-me-not,

Myosotis alpestris, the Alpine forget-me-not, found in Perthshire, likes limestone,

Myosotis sylvatica, the common forget-me-not.'

'There are ten Dad,' mother said.

'Over a dozen,' Granddad said.

'Perhaps, but there's ten in the book.'

The book was the *Concise British Herbal* and then Granddad, because he had flaking skin, would push his little finger into his ear and rotate his hand screwing up his face and saying 'Ah, well, you could be right, Na No.'

Sometimes he would use a match on his ear and then Mother would say, 'Never put anything in your ear smaller than your little finger.'

'Oh, Na No,' he would say. 'You're just like your mother.'

We never had much money but we always had

books. Mother would go to rummage sales just for the books, that was where she got *The Modern Herbal* from. She got it for threepence. She got a complete set of Arthur Mee's *Children's Encyclopaedia* for sixpence.

And then she started speaking Latin:

'Prunus spinosa, that is sloe,' she would say. 'Prunus avium, wild cherry' and then all the buttercups became 'Ranunculus' and the apples became 'Malus domestica' and my Dad said that the cat was 'Cato domestica'.

That was why she liked coming down to see Granddad, he was as mad as her on Latin names. They used to go at it hammer and tongs so that everything that was in the warehouse had two names, the Latin and the real name. My Granddad knew them both and he knew what the qualities of them all were, so that if you asked him what 'Camomile' was then he would tell you that it was part of the 'Anthemis' family' the common daisy, and that it was better than aspirin for certain things, and that if you made a tea with it then you would sleep a deep sleep and you would dream deep clear dreams and that if you soaked in the water that you used to rinse your hair, then you would think with the clarity of the Gods.

And then my mother would nod her head and she would make him a pot of tea and drink it with him inside the dusty office while my sister and I explored that part of town that went down to the cattle market and sometimes if we climbed the ladder into what was once a hay loft we would see in the distance the barely visible railway lines winding out of the town and sometimes a miniature train moving like a snake along those lines.

Nearer, behind the warehouses, we would hear

the heavy breathing of the shunting engine and the buffers of the coal trucks colliding as they were pushed into that part of the goods yard that was darkened by coal dust, the black sidings, where the coal men shovelled coal into sacks, weighed them and stacked them onto the backs of lorries.

In the Autumn my mother used to collect rose-hips from the wild rose bushes that were part of the hedgerows. The hedgerows in those days were pleached every few years, but the men who pleached the hedges would always leave the wild roses growing especially if they grew in the corner of a field. There were many rose bushes up Tinkers Hill. That was where we would pick them. Mother, my sister, the pram, to carry the picked rosehips, and the dog. We would take a picnic with us, our hens' hard boiled eggs, our apples from our trees with all the scabs and imperfections, apples that tasted like apples, cheese sandwiches cut into little squares, Welsh onions and date cake. We always had the date cake in the afternoon. I hated date cake, it was heavy and the stoneground wholemeal flour that mother used was like sawdust. I wished that my mother would use white flour with a little custard powder, like Mrs Williams did next door, but mother would not let us eat that, there was no roughage in it, we would become bunged up, we would not be regular, we would end up with cancer of the bowel.

Cancer was the price you paid for eating things you liked. It always seemed to me that my Mum liked a hard life. For example she used to wear a leather glove on her left hand but her picking hand used to become scratched and bloody. But she never seemed to mind:

'It's from the Earth,' she used to say, 'it's God's gift.'

It would take us a week to pick a half hundred-weight of hips and then we would push them in the pram down to Granddad who would weigh them and Mr Flemmings would pay her and she would have enough money to buy my sister and I a pair of shoes each that would have to last all winter and if you did not walk correctly, if you scuffed your feet then mother would shout:

'BLOOD!THOSE SHOES COST … BLOOD.'

And so you remembered her hands and you did not scuff your feet.

It was five days after Cocky had given me the half crown and it was still in my pocket and my mother never knew I had it, nor did my Dad. I had sworn on her life that I would not tell and so the half crown was almost useless, it was just there in my pocket, hot and useless, but I had told Mother that Granddad was going to get a television, that was not a secret … it was big news.

'I knew nothing about the television, Dad,' Mother said as he lifted the sack of hips from the old pram.

'I want to watch the rugby, Na No,' he said, 'and I am going down to see Mr Judd about it Saturday morning.'

'Can I come'? I asked.

It was that time in our history, in the history of our town, when Rawlings music shop sold as many pianos as televisions. It was that time when popular songs were released on sheet music and sold more copies than records. That was when you could buy a brand new clockwork gramophone. It was that time when the televisions had small screens like the sides of goldfish bowls and were housed in giant walnut veneered cabinets with twin doors that opened to reveal a great twelve inch speaker. It was that time when everything that was priced that was worth anything at all was priced in guineas. It was my childhood, it was my foundation stone, my history.

It was that time when every house had a piano, when there was someone in the house who could play very basic tunes very badly and a few who could play very nicely, thank you very much, they were the ones who were always invited to parties, or went out Saturday nights and played like my uncle did who went to live in Birmingham and for the first few months had to play in pubs and dives to live. But now Granddad who could not play the piano was left on his own, he said that the piano was gathering dust and so it was put up for sale but it never sold, instead it was taken down to the castle, to a garden fete where the main attraction was a piano breaking competition, and his piano was broken into cockwood in three minutes flat by a team from the Bull.

I saw it all in the Outer Bailey. I saw the devastating blows that were terrible to behold, the twenty-eight-pound sledge hammers and axes on a hot close summer afternoon. The heat trapped between the walls of the Inner Bailey, the black veneer splitting, the wood broken, bared until the harp-like interior was naked like the bones of a dead fish. And the final desperate sounds, like tortured notes hopelessly circulating and zigzagging into a sun-drenched pain-filled dead dull grey sky. I saw them kill Granddad's piano. And I remembered my Dad playing Fats Waller's 'Ain't Misbehavin' on that piano and I was sad and I wondered why.

I did not know then that we were rushing into the TV age. I did not know then like I do now that there would one day be TV's with over a hundred channels ... all crap.

Rawlings' music shop was divided into two. On

the left were the pianos, the radiograms and the televisions and on the right you went down a step and there was the counter where they sold sheet music and records, and things like needles for the clockwork gramophones, because you could only play a record a couple of times with each needle before it went blunt. They also sold magnetic pick-ups that fitted on the arm of the clockwork gramo-phone so that you could use the PU socket on the back of the radio and so reproduce the sounds elec-trically instead of acoustically.

Dad bought one and had a sapphire stylus fitted, it was a massive improvement. Jack Hall came down with his set of Parlophone rhythm style series, the ones with the white labels. Harry James' trumpet sounded nothing like the trumpets in the town band. The only thing wrong was that there was no way you could adjust the volume and so we sat there with a cushion over the wireless whilst Dad and Jack Hall drank cider and then when Dad and Jack had to go up to the pub to pay the club Jack decided to leave his records because he was afraid that he might drop them.

'You're right,' Dad said, 'the street lights don't have the same power as they did when they were gas. You might trip .'

Jack Hall left two cases of records at our house and that was how I found out about Duke Ellington, Stan Kenton, Louis Armstrong, Billie Holiday, Bessie Smith, Phil Harris, and even Fats Waller him-self playing and singing 'Ain't Misbehavin'. I played those records all weekend and every evening until Jack Hall came and took them back and then I was left with nothing so I joined the County Record Library and because they did not have jazz I borrowed Arthur Rubinstein playing Chopin's

Nocturnes on six twelve-inch records that were in a thick cardboard box that was heavy, too heavy for me to carry in one hand. I had to carry the box in both hands, holding it in front of me.

Classical music was heavy. I had to rewind the gramophone half way through each side. I had to work when I listened to the Nocturnes. It was deep listening, a different form of attention. Sometimes I felt that I was listening to sounds below the surface of the record so that I forgot to rewind the gramophone and all the notes slowed up and were stretched out into long low moans like dinosaurs in a primeval forest.

Mr Judd, the owner, was standing just in front of the counter wearing his pinstriped grey suit under a thick overcoat. He had a crumpled handkerchief in his hand, he was mopping his neck and then he lifted his black trilby and before he had time to wipe his head I noticed that his bald patch was sweating like a dew-drenched golf ball. Those old shopkeepers never missed a thing, and so out of the corner of his eye he saw that Granddad was standing there waiting because in those days you would never enter and wander around a shop, you waited until someone came to take care of your needs. And so it was that Mr Judd came over before he had removed his hat and coat and he held out his hand and as he shook my grandfather's hand Granddad said,

'This is my grandson,' and then I shook Mr Judd's hand. It was a hand that was soft but firm.

'One moment,' Mr Judd said. And then he removed his overcoat, his fedora trilby hat and his silk scarf and he laid them across the counter and I saw the girl from behind the counter, the one who sold Dad the magnetic pick-up, take Mr Judd's coat, hat and scarf and put them on a rack behind the office door. That was a very small thing to do for Mr Judd but it was enough.

Mr Judd and Granddad talked for about ten minutes about things that were totally unconnected with anything remotely concerning the purchase of a television set.

It was so annoying, I just could not understand why they would stand there talking about the best way to graft roses and where to get the best standards from, and then Granddad was telling Mr Judd how to fumigate a greenhouse with roll sulphur, and then I saw them both turn towards the television, and then very gently Mr Judd approached the problem of finance but withdrew when he learned that Grandfather was going to pay cash.

'Oh,' said Mr Judd, 'but you see, I do have to operate some kind of credit and do you know that it is not only the working classes,' I saw Granddad wince. 'No,' Mr Judd said removing his handkerchief from his pocket so that he could wipe his head, 'we have more of the … ah, shall we say, members of the … ah … more reputable part of our community involved in rather long term agreements, people whom you wouldn't think … now, I tell you this in strict confidence, John … it's not working tradesmen that owe me, no …'

And then they were talking together in a silent manner, my Granddad nodding fourteen to the dozen.

'Yes, John,'

'Yes indeed, Frank,'

It was a masterstroke, in one fell swoop the conversation had moved into Christian name terms. And with that we moved towards the great television set itself. When they stopped in front of the seventeen-inch model I just could not believe what I was seeing. It was not a goldfish bowl model, it was the latest seventeen-inch television. It was bigger than the one the Smiths had, and he was an electrician with his own business!

'I would not recommend anything bigger than a seventeen-inch screen, John.'

And my Granddad looked at it with his hands behind his back.

'No, it's the picture, the way it's made up, the lines moving across the screen, an hypnotic effect, not pleasant, headaches, leads to headaches, I'll get it switched on.'

And so Mr Judd had the engineer come out to switch it on and I marvelled at the fact that he himself could not even switch the thing on. The engineer had to switch it on!

And the four of us gazed at the unmoving picture of the test transmission and Mr Judd asked Granddad how far back from the TV his chair would be and then Granddad moved back to that distance and then he stood watching the test transmission and said, 'By gum, Frank, now that is a good picture.'

And Frank Judd said, 'That's the kind of picture that you'll get where you live. I have just bought an Austin van and some ladders and we have one of the best aerial men in the town and if the picture is not as good as that, John, then we'll take the set out and bring it back.'

'Oh no,' said Granddad, almost pleading that it should not be taken back, even before he'd seen it installed.

And then Mr Judd turned the sound up so that the music that you could only hear on a television test transmission began to fill the showroom. And you could see faintly the outline of a huge twelve-inch speaker hiding behind a gold fabric surface and the name 'Baird' was embossed on a gold badge underneath the seventeen-inch screen. It was such a beautiful television, it was the very latest, the screen was almost flat.

'John,' said Mr Judd, pointing to the name 'Baird'. 'He was the man who invented television, and what is more, John, you will not get a better sound than what is coming from that speaker', and then he paused as if he was looking for inspiration to fall from the heavens, and then he said,

'A male voice choir, fer instance.'

And my Grandfather thought about the time when he went to Cardiff Arms Park and the stadium full to the brim sang 'Abide with Me'. And Mr Judd knew by looking at Granddad that he had sold him a sixty-nine guinea television set.

And my Grandfather offered his hand and he shook Frank Judd's hand and he thanked him for selling him a television, and the engineer went behind the counter and taking a large white label he wrote 'Hobbs sold' on it. And when Granddad reached into his inside pocket for the money that he had in his wallet, Mr Judd said:

'When it is installed and you are satisfied, then you will come down here and pay me.'

'I will,' said Granddad and they were both shaking hands again.

And Mr Judd knew that Granddad would pay him and Granddad knew that he would pay Mr Judd. They both knew that even if Titterstone erupted like it did before there were Dinosaurs walking on the surface of the Earth then Granddad would pay his debt, not fire, nor water, even death would not prevent payment of that debt because that was how it was in those days ... they had trust and they respected each other.

When we got back outside, I noticed little whirlwinds of dust visible and rising from the cobblestones each side of Broad Street.

And then Granddad said to me:

'I get very lonely sometimes since your grandmother passed away, sometimes I talk to myself, I talk because I'm afraid of being alone. The television will help ... at least I hope it will.'

And then Granddad offered me his hand and I took it and I noticed that behind each knuckle on Granddad's fingers there were thick colonies of black hairs. He also had the same kind of hairs growing out of his ears.

# 15 *A Cosmic Context*

In 1952 I had to sit the examination that would allow me entrance to the Grammar school. If I passed then I would have a new bicycle. If I failed then I would have to continue with the hoop. I wanted a new bike but I did not want to go to the Grammar school, anyway I was no good at mathematics so I just looked out of the window and counted the bricks on the wall opposite. It was a mistake. I had to wait until Christmas for the bike and everybody was deciding what I should be when I left school. And all I wanted to be was an engine driver and you did not have to go to Grammar school to be an engine driver, you had to be a fireman first and then after a few years you could be an engine driver. If you started on the railway as a guard then you would not end up as an engine driver, if you did anything else on the railway other than a fireman then you would not be an engine driver. I knew how you became an engine driver but you had to be eighteen to be a fireman. That meant that there was three years between the time you left school and the time that you could get onto the footplate. And what was more when you got to the age of eighteen you were conscripted into the Army. It was a trap. It was a big problem because you would then come out after two years without a trade. This fact did not worry me since all I wanted to be was an engine driver. But it did worry my mother and father who wanted me to get a trade. They were also worried about the catch-you-kill-you-tribe in Kenya and another war in Cyprus. They did not want me to go into the Army.

It was a hell of a time, they were building a dozen aluminium bungalows next to our house where the fire had been and since I spent a lot of time on the site during the summer holidays holding the staff so that levels could be taken and riding in the tipper lorry that brought the sand from the quarry and working out how they set out a house so that, when my Dad decided to build a concrete base for a chicken run, I told him that you always started from the northeast corner, because that was the corner that they started when they built King Solomon's temple and that no matter what you built then you always started from that corner;

'Who told you that?' Dad asked.

'Mr Gough,' I said. 'Doesn't matter what you build, even if it's a septic tank, you always start from that corner,' I said.

'He'll make a good bricklayer,' Dad said to my mother later. And so the die was cast, and I did not care because I thought that it would only be until I was eighteen and could then be a fireman.

*EDWARD, GEORGE AND HENRY*

We had a broody Bantam hen and Dad and I went up to Vashon Twiddy's to buy half a dozen eggs.

He held each egg an inch away from a lighted candle, turned them a little, discarded one, wrapped them individually in newspaper and put them into an old shoe box:

'Them are all fertilised,' he said.

And we believed him because he used to read from a black fire and brimstone bible every Saturday afternoon just outside the town hall.

Five hatched. 'That was because she was a Bantam and her little bum was just not big enough,' my mother said. 'You ask too much of a woman,' she said.

And so three little balls of yellow fluff became cocks and two little balls of yellow fluff became hens. Those cocks fought one with the other until they were a sorry sight. And they crowed and squawked and Mrs Hen and her daughters were chased and pecked until their poor little arseholes were red raw.

Mother used to mix all the scraps from the house, anything edible she made into a mash with bran and those cocks would gobble it down until they almost choked, and Dad and I used to watch them eating, Dad shouting encouragement, 'Good boys,' he used to say, 'nothing like a good cock for Christmas.'

Two days before the festival I held a Tilley lamp that roared and hissed and Dad grabbed George and then he tied his legs together and he hung him from a butcher's hook in the shed and then he took the sharp knife and he stuck George, and then George flapped his wings, and he pumped his blood into an old bucket and I watched, holding the dog's ear, and the smell of the blood mixed with the smells of the hanging tobacco leaves was a red smell, thick and sticky.

'He dunna feel a thing,' Dad said, 'that's only his nerves. I'll get Ted.'

But Dad came back with Henry.

'Do ya wanta stick Henry?' Dad asked.

I held the knife, but Henry looked at me with his one eye.

'I canna do it,' I cried, and I ran outside closing the door behind me.

'LEAVE THE DOOR OPEN!' Dad shouted.

And so I opened the door, and Dad said, 'Always leave the door open, it makes it easier fer their little souls to get out.'

'I'm sorry,' I said.

'It danna matter,' Dad said. 'You follers yer mother, her's like that.'

For Christmas I got a pair of binoculars that Dad had found advertised in the *Exchange and Mart*. Real ex-Army binoculars, they were in fact ex-Navy, which made them better because they would have been used on the bridge of a ship and could magnify things sixty times. I took them straight up to the railway line and waited for an hour until a 'Grange' class locomotive 'Bodicote' No. 6870 came out of the tunnel and I saw the rivets on the buffer beam so clearly that I could count that there were four each side and the oval disc at the bottom of the smoke box said 84 G. By God, they were good binoculars and I saw the whites of the driver's eyes before he saw me and I saw the grease on the valve gear of that locomotive, so that that almost empty passenger train became a closely observed thing and I wanted to wait for another train but it was Christmas day and hardly any trains ran then.

Granddad said that they were good fowl and that you could not beat a good backyard cock, but my sister declared that she was now a vegetarian and then after we'd all listened to the Queen, Father and I went to feed the rabbits and the rest of the chickens and Edward was strutting about the pen and the feathers around the hens' backsides had started to grow. It was almost four in the afternoon and bitter cold, and the day had slipped away and I stood there as the half-light moved towards me, with part of George inside my belly.

It was not a pleasant Christmas day.

A pleasant Christmas day it was not.

After Christmas I started to study the stars. It was the winter nights, those small walks from our back door to the shed. Cold frosty evenings and above me the bright chromed stars so that everything became bigger and the craters on the moon had rims and walls, and my hands were so cold that I cut the fingers off an old pair of gloves but the colder it was the clearer it was and so I took the tiles off the old pigsty and lay there watching the universe from an old deck chair surrounded by straw. It looked to me then that the Milky Way was the backbone of the night and that without it all the other stars would come crashing down.

But the only things that fell were shooting stars. I searched the skies for them, followed them and more than once ran outside just as they disappeared over the horizon expecting to hear a great crash.

It was that time when Granddad used to come down to our house every Sunday for his lunch. Once I told him that the moon was four billion years old and was two hundred and thirty-eight thousand miles away and moved at two thousand miles an hour around the earth. He went mad and said that the world was flat. He used to lie back in the best armchair and snore the afternoon away. One afternoon I built a model of the earth and the moon using an orange and an apple suspended on fishing line just over his head. I made the sun shine from a flash lamp so that the shadow was day and night.

I remember him in that chair then and now, him with his blue-veined nose and yellowish false teeth moving up and down as the air came out of his mouth so that as he woke and saw the sun, the earth and the moon hanging there, those teeth flew out and landed on his chest just as he was waking and all his gums had imploded so that his words were muffled, him looking for his teeth that had slipped down the side of the chair where sometimes the dog sat. All those hairs attached to his false teeth but him in such a temper that he clapped them right into his mouth,

'THE WORLD IS FLAT' he shouted.

And then the hairs started to tickle his throat and he was coughing and barking like a dog and he was all red -faced and his great nose was purple.

It only takes one hair in the back of your throat to make you mad but he had a whole mouthful.

Down on his hands and knees he went, his teeth already on the floor, they were moving those teeth, leading a life of their own, until my mother picked them up with the tea towel.

'You'll want to sterilize that before you dry another dish with it,' my Dad said.

And then Granddad went so mad that we all thought that he was having a fit, but I could not stop tittering and started to laugh until my mother flicked the tea towel at me and caught me just right so that my cheek stung.

'That serves you right,' Dad said. 'You'd laugh if yer mother's arse was on fire.'

Then we all started to laugh, even my mother, who was helping Granddad to his feet and steering him into the kitchen where he had to gargle half a dozen times to remove the final hair and then when he finally made his entrance and saw the orange and the apple still hanging from the ceiling he shouted,

'THE BLOODY WORLD IS FLAT AND THAT'S AN END TO IT'.

That was the week the first UFO was sighted over the Stiperstones. It was when they found an old Humber car with a flat battery standing in the middle of the road with the driver and the passenger door open. Fifty yards in front of that car was a burnt patch of Tarmac. From the side of the road stretching right across to the Stiperstone Rocks was a ploughed ridge where the craft had landed. Six people saw the cigar-shaped craft that looked like a Zeppelin hover less than a few feet over the tops of the rocks ... and then it was gone.

Two weeks later a man from Church Stretton was found wandering around the Stiperstones looking for a Humber car. 'It was the lights,' he said. He was looking for the lights. He was confused, he was taken to hospital and given electric shock treatment to straighten him out. A few weeks later on two separate occasions a black Buick car was seen parked outside his house.

The Stiperstones was the perfect place for a sighting. It was haunted by Wild Edric who was the last Saxon to fight William the Conqueror. He was such a good Saxon soldier that he had to be killed three times and had to be buried under the lead mine, which is beneath the Devil's chair. They had to do all that to Wild Edric to stop him from rising.

All that part of our county is weird and full of strange customs so that even now you will see on the barbed wire fences dead crows and moles and sometimes dead lambs in the forks of trees because some still believe that if lambs are buried then half the lambs born later will be born dead. And even now there are very few farmers who will go near the cowshed on Christmas eve because that is the time when all the cattle bow down on one knee to honour the birth of Christ in the stable. If you see that happen then you die. And everyone knows that on the longest day then all the ghosts of the county meet right on the top of the Stiperstones and that the faint white cloud that hangs over there on the night of the longest day is in fact Ectoplasm. But it was something more solid than that that made the tarmac burn.

I wanted to see a UFO but I was so afraid that I would see one that I lay in the old pigsty covered in old Army blankets with the dog at my side. It was very difficult, the more I concentrated the more the dog licked my face, it was terrible, all my thoughts going out into the sky so that UFO's would be attracted to me lying there. Me, myself, all my senses heightened, the tranquillity of my pigsty, absorbing the intimacy of the stars, the shadows from the moon moving so slowly in the branches of the old apple tree. The minute sound of a mouse running across the rafters and a moth fluttering across the open roof, landing right on the edge of the picture in my mind as it focused on the patterns of light, shadow, smell, and the silence in-between the trains. I knew that they would never come to me lying there in that straw at the foot of a railway embankment, the trains would frighten them away.

## THE HEIGHT OF THE SUN

'What do any of you know about the height of the sun?' asked Mr Lambull, our science teacher.

'It's farthest away in the summer but higher in the sky,' I answered.

It was the correct answer and so we went out onto the lawn next to the snake pit, our science teacher carrying the theodolite so that we could measure the height of the sun and when Mr Lambull asked if anyone could assemble the thing. I did it because it was the same kind of instrument that Mr Gough used to make levels on the site, it was just that the instrument that screwed onto its top was different, more like a protractor for measuring the angle of the sun. I could do it, it was simple, I could do it better than the science master. But what happened next was that I volunteered to take the height of the sun every day for a year.

I would have to come out onto the lawn past the domestic science classroom, past the woodwork room, set up the theodolite, make a few notes, take it down and then enter the reading onto a graph. I would have to do it at midday Greenwich Mean Time every day for a year. That meant in the summer I would have to do it at eleven am and Mr Lambull would arrange with all the other teachers that I should leave whatever class I was in to enable me to complete the task.

And then it was Coronation day and Edmund Hillary climbed Everest with Sherpa Tenzing. It was the most important event of the year, it was the result of team effort. Everest was the highest mountain in the world and an Englishman had climbed it, because only an Englishman could have done it, and therefore we must be proud to be English, an Englishman on the roof of the world, completely forgetting that Edmund Hillary was from New Zealand and Sherpa Tenzing took the photograph.

Bill Summers our school boss saw an achievement so vast that his imagination started to work overtime. He decided that the whole of the side of the main hall should be a painting of the summit of Everest. That a life size portrait of Hillary would be painted up there. Gallons of white paint for the snow, gallons of blue paint for the sky and gallons of grey paint were obtained. We would then be able to stand during morning assembly singing and praying and all the time, that great event seeping into our young minds so that when we went forth into the world we would be better citizens because an Englishman had achieved something marvellous. We were young Elizabethans, and we had to be proud of it. And so when the thing was finished we all had to sing 'Land of Hope and Glory' and 'Abide with Me,'

I was in the school choir but could not sing. It was a fluke. Dave Lewis sat next to me in class and had a very powerful voice. I could not sing so I just opened and closed my mouth, miming the words. Miss Rogers our music teacher was partly deaf and stood next to me one day. I was opening and closing my mouth, 'Good', she said, 'but not so loud.' I was selected, Lewis was not, and I did not know how to tell her that it was him who'd done the singing.

Miss Rogers was so old that she'd taught my father to write. She must have been young then, she could have been beautiful, she might have been slim, she probably did not have puffy fingers like short sausages that made you move away when she poked you.

The height of the sun saved me. I told her that I had to leave at eleven o'clock every day. 'You won't have time to be in the choir,' she said. 'No Miss', I said. And everyone who thought that I was an idiot to volunteer for such a thing changed their minds.

It was at about this time that the aluminium bungalows were finished. The Midland Red Bus company had also built a bus garage at the bottom of Weeping Cross Lane. There was such a shortage of drivers that new families from Birmingham moved in to the finished bungalows. One family had three girls, one my age, one was younger and the other was older. The oldest had breasts that looked like pears. I'd seen them because our street used to play rounders in a field, a field that is now a housing estate. She used to lean forward when she was fielding and her breasts swung inside her loose blouse. They were the most beautiful things that I had ever seen in my life. They were more beautiful than the Bassett Lowke steam engine in the latest catalogue and I wanted that more than anything else in the world.

At the bottom of our field was a valley and a stream, this stream ran into a tunnel that went under the railway line. Where the valley folded, oak and ash trees grew. It faced in a north westerly direction and so the bank was all thick with moss and lichens hung from the trunks of the trees. On each side of the stream were Sally trees. We had built a camp in the crown of the biggest tree. It had taken us all the Easter holiday to build, we'd wrapped the branches into a lattice work and then the tree grew around the lattice so that three of us could hide. It was our secret place, there was an old tin travelling trunk that contained five 'Turf' cigarettes, tobacco from my Dad's shed, one quart of cider, the broken blade from a 'lambs foot' pen knife, a full length pin up from the centre of *Blighty* and a pig's bladder. These were all common property that belonged to the camp.

One Tuesday evening we were so busy smoking our cigarettes that we did not see the woman who worked in the false teeth factory walking hand in hand with a soldier in RAF uniform. We were too busy sharing the knob pin that we used to stick in the butt end of the fags so that we could smoke the butt of cigarette completely away. She was swinging a brown handbag and then he started to laugh, he was laughing like a hyena and then they both started to laugh and she was saying that she would not go down there.

'There's moss and it's soft,' he said.

'That's why,' she said.

And then they started to laugh again, we were so completely caught up in our smoking that they were only about thirty feet away before we realised that they were so near. We could not move. We froze. You could have heard a pin drop in our tree house. And then they started to kiss each other. I looked at Spud, he looked at Eric, we all looked at each other and then we looked at the couple under the ash tree kissing each other, her holding him behind his head so that she was forcing his face onto hers.

'I'm going,' I whispered.

'You can't,' Spud whispered. 'He'll see you.'

'I'll run,' I whispered.

'He'll catch one of us,'Eric said.

'Shush,' I said.

We were trapped in our own tree. Spud Taylor made a gesture of despair and shook his head. Eric who was looking over the edge of the lattice fence saw them roll over and then he waved his arms beckoning us so that we all looked and saw her on top of him and then we saw his hands roll up her skirt and she was laughing and then she lifted herself up and we saw his hands peel her knickers off her backside. Her knickers were just like my mother's, they were pink and had legs, but her backside was white and the way that she was sitting on him it looked like if she was all bum and then she reached around and pulled her skirt back over her bare bum so that all we could see was her hands holding his head. She was running her hands through his hair so that his hair stood up. He had shiny black hair that looked as if it had been doused in motor oil. She was squatting on him and then they rolled over so that they rolled away from her handbag and then he was on top of her and they were kissing each other again. And then he stood up and turned away from her and he walked towards our tree so that we froze, we could not move we just had to watch him. He started to pee, he peed like a horse all the time pulling on his penis so that when he had finished it was bigger than it was when he had started and then he started to fish something out of his trouser pocket.

'He's looking for a Johnny,' Spud whispered.

It was not that warm an evening but we saw that the man was sweating as he started to roll the thing onto the end of his penis. He rolled it like we did when we put tight football socks on.

we were about to watch copulation unseen from the safety of our tree

we were sinking into the delights of the voyeur

we were more sinful than the sinner

and there was nothing that we could do about it

When he went back to the woman who was lying waiting he did a strange thing, he put his head between her legs and she was holding his head and every time he started to lift his head she was holding it and moaning until he had to fight her to get back on top of her. It was terrible, he was hurting her but she would not let go and then all we could see was his backside moving up and down and she was holding a handful of moss in each hand and moaning until he started to cry out and we could not tell who was hurting the other most. When they finished they lay there torturing us, it was the longest time in our lives that we had not moved and we could not move and then a goods train went by and the driver blew his whistle and as that train went by they got up and she gathered up her handbag and stepped into her knickers and they walked back the way they came, him his hair all roughed up holding her as they walked across the field.

As soon as they were out of sight we climbed out of the tree.

'That's how they make babies,' Spud said .

'Then why do they wear this?' Eric said poking at the knotted Johnny with a stick.

'So that they won't have one,' Spud said, 'that's the seed, from his balls, it floats.'

'I know,' I said.

'You been wanking in the bath', Spud whispered.

And then I knew that Spud and I knew more about it than Eric who was two months older than us. But Eric had had rheumatic fever and had had a whole year off school and for one reason or another he had had his foreskin removed. It was called circumcision, Jews had it done to them when they were born so that they were always clean. It stopped them rubbing the end of their dicks, it stopped them getting warts on their hands. But there were no Jews to speak of in our town so we never saw any Jewish hands, just a small sect of British Israelites that were as far as we were concerned like the Christian Scientists, and since we had never seen any of them naked we did not know very much about them, but we were intact and could hold our skin at the end when we peed and make a balloon.

Eric could pee higher than us even though his penis was smaller than ours.

'It was that illness that you had,' said Spud, 'you went into hibernation fer a year, that's what it was.'

But I knew that it was the removal of that skin that prevented him from playing with his penis. And so we let him have the first drag of the last 'Turf' cigarette. We let him stand there with it between his lips like Humphrey Bogart did when he watched the plane leave. It was important for him to do that because we all had feelings ticking away under our shirts like an alarm clock waiting to go off, the madness and terror of knowing that after what we'd seen nothing would ever be the same again.

'I'm never going to get married,' Spud said.

'Nor me,' I said.

'You might have to,' Eric said.

'Na,' Spud said.

'If you make one pregnant, then you have to,' Eric said and he passed his cigarette to Spud who took a deep long drag and then tried to make smoke rings, he was good at making smoke rings. Eric and I watched him make two.

As the sun began to lose its grip on the rim of the sky the clouds over Whitcliffe turned into a pinkish red.

'Let's go,' I said.

We were sad, sad with the new knowledge that we were carrying home with us.

And it worried me that perhaps my parents had made me like that, I wanted to believe that it was different for them. It was just that I could not imagine my mother moaning and crying and holding moss in her hands, I tried to believe that it had not happened like that. But I knew that it did happen like that because I'd seen dogs doing it and I saw a horse do it and the old buck rabbit used to do it as soon as he got in with a doe. Animals did it almost like I'd just seen humans doing it. It was frightening to think that one day I would have to do it.

That night I dreamt that I was holding the girl with the breasts like pears, we were on the bank of a river, I had saved her, all the people were cheering but my belly was all wet and sticky.

# 16 *Wednesday*

It was on a Wednesday morning during gardening. We were digging the garden that ran alongside the Friars Walk. The trouble was that the garden was all stones, not much soil. It was very difficult to dig. Only an old foolish schoolteacher like Mr Keyse could dig it – well, I suppose my Dad would have been able to dig it, or Tony's Dad, a grown up mind would make a good job of it. Yes, it required that kind of mind. Old Man Weaver had walked down the Friars Walk right next to where we were digging and he'd stopped and watched us. We could feel him mentally making a note of every movement that we made.

'Mind you dana get a blister on yer hand,' he'd said, and then he'd laughed as if we were not doing it right.

We *were* doing it right, we knew how to do it. You had to push the fork in and wriggle it round the stones and then you had to take the stones out, and you had to take the weeds out as well. We knew how. It was just hard work and when Old Man Weaver came back and said, 'You ain't done much, 'ave yer?' Tony said 'Balls.'

And Old Man Weaver said, 'What did you say?

And Tony said 'Netball, the girls are playing netball.'

And we knew that he knew that we knew that he used to stand watching the girls playing netball, with his right hand in his pocket ... but we kept our heads bent, giggling as Old Man Weaver shuffled up the path mumbling, 'God 'elp this country if there's another war.'

We had a great pile of stones, Tony Williams and I, and a small pile of weeds. It was proof that we had been working. We reckoned that we had enough stones and weeds to justify a morning's work so we started mucking about. We started throwing stones across the playground and then Tony threw his fork at me and it went right through my foot.

My foot went wet. It was the blood. I just stood there, the fork sticking right through my shoe. Almost new shoes and there was no pain, just the wetness.

'Oh balls,' Tony shouted, 'we'll get the cane, we'll get six conduct marks and we'll be caned.'

'You will, idiot,' I shouted. 'You did it,' and then I thought for a moment that Tony was going to cry.

'Don't cry,' I said, 'just get the fork out.'

And so he pulled the fork out and I walked over to the steps near to the stone carving of the Prince of Wales' feathers that my Granddad had done in 1925 and I sat down and took my shoe and then my sock off. The fork had gone through the top of the shoe and in between my toes. It was the only time in my life that I thanked God that my mother bought me shoes that were a size too big so that I would grow into them. There was a little blood but nothing really wrong. It was not as dramatic as it looked when it happened and Tony promised to give me a pocket knife if I said nothing but we had arithmetic next and so I put my shoe and sock back on and walked back to where it had happened and pushed the fork back into my foot.

'Go and get Miss Baker,' I shouted. But Tony wouldn't .

'I'll say that it was an accident,' I said.

But then I had to promise and cross my heart and wish to die and almost plead before Tony would go. So that was how Tony finally went and got Miss Baker who did not believe him because he was almost silent when he told her, whispering in her ear. When she did come out she almost fainted when she saw the fork sticking in my foot. And then she ran back inside to get Mr Keyse who came and pulled the fork out so that I was dancing about on one leg and shouting that it hurt. And then I had to remove my sock and both teachers bent and looked at how the fork had grazed the skin between each toe.

'Take him to the clinic,' Mr Keyse told Tony .

And that was how I hopped up Galdeford until we were out of sight of the school and then we walked around Woolworths and then we walked to the Picture House and we saw that *High Noon* was showing Thursday, Friday and Saturday. And then we hung about a bit, but we had to go to the clinic.

The clinic was where the school dentist was, it was where you had your injections. But I'd never had any injections. My mother would not allow injections, she said that doctors did not tell you everything about injections and that there were side effects that would leave you weaker than if you'd not had them and that it was better not to have them because later on in life your immune system would be weaker if you'd had them so she would never let us have them. Instead we had to play with children who had had measles and that's how I caught all the known diseases except chicken pox. I could never catch that.

My mother did not like the school doctor who examined us every year and all the time kept going on at my mother about the need for injections and my mother all the time going on about the fact that injections were destroying the immune system and I had to stand there naked while they called each other's tune.

My Mum was the only one who came when we were examined. Very few mums came, the school doctor just did the examinations and gave the injections and that was that and I wished that we could be a normal family and not have opinions about things. I hated the nurse who was always dressed in blue and looked in your hair for nits and then said to me when it was my turn, 'You have not had any injections, you had better stand over there and I'll make a note to take to your mother. It's not right that you should be in the same class as those who have had their injections.' And so I had to take a note home from the nurse and give it to my mother who would rant on and on about the fact that if you were treated with Homeopathic medicine then you would never need injections.

My mother was strange. She was told that she would need glasses but instead went to the Indian eye doctor who taught her to sit with her legs crossed in the middle of the floor in her bedroom in the sunlight and recite:

'There is a healing light shining in the centre of my Being.'

And that was not all. When my Dad caught her doing her meditations she said, 'The biggest obstacle to seeing is the eye.'

That floored my Dad who went up to the shed to drink cider and study Pataphysics. If I'd have realised that I'd have ended up in the clinic and have to see that nurse then I would not have stuck the fork back in my foot, but it was too late, that was why I'd walked around Woolworths but it was no good it had only delayed the arrival at the clinic by about ten minutes.

'You were very lucky,' Nurse said as she plastered my foot in iodine.

It hurt worse than any pain that I had ever experienced but I never cried.

'Now we'll give you a tetanus injection,' she said. And then I got so afraid of what my mother would say that I started to tremble.

'I can't,' I shouted. 'I'll have to fetch my Mum.'

'You'll get lockjaw,' the nurse said.

'I don't care,' I said. I was almost crying. 'I have to fetch my Mum.'

And I ran out of that clinic so fast that I left my shoe behind.

We sat around the castle, me sitting there with only one shoe.

'You know what happens when you get lockjaw,' Tony said.

'Naw,' I said.

'Yer jaw seizes up and you bite yer tongue off and you locks yer jaw,' Tony said.

I thought about what he said and tried to imagine what it would be like to have lockjaw, to be unable to move your mouth. and I tried to think of someone who had had lockjaw, but there was no one and what was more there was no one who I knew who knew anyone who had ever had lockjaw, in fact it was one of those things that no one ever had, to my mind it was deader than the Do-Do bird, but you never knew if the nurse was telling the truth, it was just that most believed what she said, except my mother. I would have to get home to my mother who would give me Arnica. Arnica was powerful. I would be all right with Arnica.

'You have to go back for my shoe,' I said, but Tony would not go back.

'I'll tell that it was you,' I said.

'You promised,' Tony said.

'Go and get the shoe,' I said.

And then I had to promise that I would give him a piece of cake, an apple and a Jew's harp.

'Take me to the camp,' he said.

All he wanted was to go to the camp, but he had no right to ask that, he knew the rules about camps. But he knew that we had the best camp.

'I can't,' I said, 'it's between Eric, Spud and me.' But in the end I had to promise to take him because I had to have my shoe, and so he went for my shoe, coming back with it five minutes later.

'What did she say?' I asked.

'Nothing, there was nobody there,' Tony said, 'I just took it.'

We walked around the Town Hall twice. We saw that there would be a dance in aid of the Labour Party that featured Ken Mackintosh and his Orchestra. And there was a poster advertising a concert party in the Zion Methodist church hall. My Dad was part of that concert party, he used to do what he called a 'Turn' which meant that he would tell jokes about how the vicar found a wart on a cow's udder and he would at just the right moment shout at the audience,

'Did you know that the ostrich is the only bird in the world that can bend down, stick its head through its back legs and whistle through the whole of the afternoon ... did you know that?'

Dad was so good at it that they always laughed and then he would ask someone in front to take their gloves off so that they could clap louder, and then they would laugh even louder, and Bill Jane who was the compere and played the mouth organ would be trying to get Dad off the stage before he said something that was too near the mark but that was an almost impossible thing to do since Dad would have been taking swigs from an old stone jar full of a mixture of cider and whisky.

My Dad loved to do a turn even if it was for the Methodist church, the only trouble was that it was what he called a dry turn, but he'd solved that problem with the stone jar and anyway the next act was Harry Lewis who was known to have a liking for Shakespeare, he would be liable to break out in an excerpt from one or two of the Bard's plays in any order that he thought fit.

'I'll be back,' my Dad would shout as he left the stage. He was shouting that phrase at the audience 30 years before Schwarzenegger was born.

When we came around the Town Hall for the third time we went over to the Picture House and saw that they had put out the posters for Saturday afternoon's matinee. This Saturday it was to be the Marx Brothers *Duck Soup*.

Of all the buildings in our town the two cinemas were the most important to us. It was where we escaped reality.

There were always two films at each show, an A film, a B film, and then the newsreel. And we sat throughout the lot. It did not matter how bad the B film was, we sat through it, and by God there were some bad B films …

But we all loved the way the hero tore off his belt buckle as he rammed open the flapping doors and kicked some poor critter as he bent over and all the time the honky tonk piano banging out those songs, and then somebody shot out the drinks bottles behind the bar one by one and then before he went outside our hero spat into the silver spittoon before he stared down at the great uplifted bosoms of a bar room girl and our mouths watered and we saw the evil sheriff standing there down at the end of the road and he was shaking like he had Saint Vitus Dance until the first slug mercifully stiffened him ...

Yes, yes and the Good Lord willing and the creeks don't rise, I'll see ya agin some time ...

And then we walked out past the portraits of all the great movie stars, Clark Gable, Victor McLaglen, Gary Cooper, James Cagney, Kim Novak, Humphrey Bogart, Doris Day and Jane Russell. Jane had the curves, beautiful curves.

'An ideal woman, so my Dad says,' Tony said.

'Who?' I asked.

'Jane Russell,' Tony said.

We both thought about it for a while and I wondered what Jane Russell would look like if she had nothing on at all, would they be like Mrs Gruntorad's who was married to a Czech, a friend of my mother's, who used to feed her baby outside her back door flopping each breast out one at a time, would Jane Russell's nipples be as big as Mrs Gruntorad's? It was something to think about ... because the sun was burning down on the pavement outside the Town Hall, and Jim Stokes was looking at us looking at the pictures in the Picture House. Well, he could carry on looking ... he would tell my Dad, he would tell Tony's Dad,

'They was looking in the Picture House when they should have been at school,' he would say.

But we had an excuse we had just been to the clinic because I'd had a fork stuck in my foot.

It was a quarter to twelve when we got back to

school, just in time for me to take the height of the sun. The whole class looked at me as we passed the window, me limping, but not too much, Tony carrying the tripod behind me. I felt important as I explained how to set the thing up and then we watched the sun shining over our town and we watched the girls playing netball and they looked so good in their shorts and that was the best part, all those legs going right up to those backsides and those small hard breasts like tennis balls moving beneath T shirts as they reached up to put the ball in the net. It was marvellous to think that there were so many girls in our school. The problem was how to get near them, how to approach them because you did not really know what it was that you wanted from them and so you kept away from them as best you could.

And then the fire siren went off, but it was Wednesday. Wednesday was practice day. Our town is too small to have full time firemen, we have part timers. If there is a fire then the siren goes off on the top of the old police station and all the firemen drop whatever they are doing and race down to the fire station on bicycles, Carpenters drop their planes, the plumber stops wiping a joint on a pipe and if Bob Gee is serving you an ice cream then he just stops serving an ice cream and he leaves you standing there in the shop because Bob Gee is always first at the fire station, his ice cream shop and cafe is opposite and he is always first at a fire and if it's after school or in the holidays then as many children as firemen race to the fire station and somebody shouts:

'Where's the fire?' and somebody will shout back: 'Up Rock Lane.'

And as the old red Dennis fire engine pulls out of

the station spilling a little water a fireman will shout:

'It's only a chimney.'

But no matter. The fire engine will be followed by children on bicycles. But today is Wednesday and as soon as Tony says, 'Bit long fer a practice, in it,' the siren slowly dies at the end of its long scream and every one in our town looks back at whatever they were doing and Galdeford explodes into three hundred children released from the prison of school and already those at the top part of the school are waiting in line for two big dollops of mashed potato, two slices of warm beef and diced carrots all covered in brown gravy. But not me. I had to go home. I never had school dinners. And so we made a note of the height of the sun and then we packed everything up and walked towards the science room. Me forgetting to limp.

# 17   *Pig Day*

I saw them coming up Old Street, a herd of prime Hereford bullocks, about fifty head, and Black Jack's three point Border collie working that herd like the good bitch she was. Shopkeepers standing in doorways rubbing their hands, looking, removing anything that might get in the way. Dustbins and tools leaning outside the window of Rickards the ironmongers were taken and stacked up the alley. The shops almost shutting, barricading, and the policeman directing the traffic on the Bull Ring waving his arms at cars to pull over because a herd was coming to market and nothing was going to stop cattle goaded from the rear by Black Jack wearing his shit-stained rubber sou'wester, matching jacket and trousers, same ensemble, winter or summer.

Black Jack smelt. Strange parasites lived between Jack's skin and his rubber raiment. He lived under hedges or bedded down next to his herd. He was one of the last drovers to use the old Iron Age tracks that lead all the way to the Welsh coast. He was half the price of a cattle truck, and unlike a cattle truck that gives off toxic diesel fumes, Jack only swore if you shouted at him.

Mind you, you never shouted at him if he was without a herd, you steered clear of him when he was on his own. Even if you had no intention of shouting at him you walked on the other side of the road because he just might strike you with his stick because he would probably not remember if it was you who had shouted at him. All children were guilty, we all shouted at him and we all avoided him, and if he did hit you then your parents would say, 'I told you to keep out of his way, serves you right, he might have done ya a bit of good'!

Up and over the Bull Ring they came and up they reared, standing on hind legs like begging dogs, some attempting copulation, giant pantomime beasts, six-legged monsters, berserk, out of control, nostrils blowing, like Chinese dragons, snot flying, bellowing, and Jack shouting:

'DOWN, YOU BASTARDS ... DOWN. GET DOWN.'

His stick going Crack across the beasts' backs.

'YOU DIRTY FILTHY EVIL BLACK ENAM-ELLED BASTARD.'

Crack ... crack ... crack the stick went, across the animal's back, until its sexual urges fell back into the recess of its castrated bovine mind. Jack's herd was late, dozens of others had arrived hours before. The cattle pens were full. You could hear the animals moaning down in the auction yard.

I liked market day, pig day. I liked to hear the auctioneer shouting out the price, it echoed beneath the sheep shed, it was like an opera singer singing, it was the rhythm. I'd go down there after I'd taken the height of the sun just to listen to the auctioneer chanting but first I wanted to look in Woolworths and anyway today was a big pig, which meant that the pubs would be open all day, it meant that there would be stalls outside the Town Hall as well as inside.

And so all the excitement from the herd moved on down Corve Street to the market and all the dust and money the market brought settled once again on our town's piss wet streets.

Ours is a market town. Take the market out, and there is no town. That's all there is to it, everybody knows, no shite, no money, everybody knows.

And then there was a silence, and then the shop-keepers started to place things back out onto the street in front of their shops and as I walked past the saddler's I looked through the window and saw a well dressed man holding a saddle and I saw that the great fat ginger tom cat was fast asleep in the sun-filled hottest part of the shop's window and as I passed the doorway I smelt the shop which smelt of good-quality leather, dubbing and other comforting odours.

Standing in front of the Butter Cross were Jim Stokes, Joe Wait and Manny Weaver. Jim Stokes was a caretaker at the High School. He always wore shorts and looked like an ancient scout-master. Jim was a keep fit maniac. When he was a young man he used to swim in the river 365 mornings of the year. Crowds used to gather on the bank when he broke the ice in winter, they stood there just to see him plunge in, half expecting that he would not resurface.

'Warmer down there than out here,' he would say as he dried himself, standing on the ice. It was true but nobody believed it.

Next to him, Joe Wait the undertaker. His name was always called out at the pictures when a cowboy got shot on the silver screen:

'Fetch Joe Wait,' someone would shout, or, 'There's another fer Joe Wait'.

Next to him was Manny Weaver who made a

living collecting bean sticks on the Whitcliffe Common. He used to have a donkey cart connected to a moke. Behind those three just behind the stone pillars stood three more men whose names I did not know, just that they were standing there pulling their braces with their thumbs and watching everything that moved in front of them. And then coming down the High Street pushing his carrier bike was my father with Cocky Wontner who was also pushing his bike, but his bike never had a carrier, because he was the foreman. He carried a pencil behind his ear instead.

They would stop and talk with the men who were watching from the steps of the Butter Cross. Everyone stopped and talked in those days, they were never in a hurry:

'What's the hurry?' somebody would shout if you were to pass by without stopping, or; 'Where's the fire?'. Everybody knew everybody. A stranger stood out like a sore spot. There were no secrets. Dad reckoned that Mrs Poole knew how many times people farted in bed.

And there were no worries in those days about anything, never mind your weight. If you were fortunate enough to have a hanging beer gut then that meant that it was something that had taken a few years to cultivate, it was a friend. It was not unusual to see men holding their gut with both hands and caressing it in a very tender way, in fact if you had had a beer belly and then lost it, people would talk and say things like:

'Shame fer uld Bill, lost some weight, under the Doctor, be better fer him if he put some back.'

The fact was that people in those days did put weight on especially during the summer, it was as if they were storing it to tide them over a bad winter.

And when the pubs were open they drank in a hearty way, the way Yeomen did, swilling beer or cider down without shame as if they were bulwarking themselves against the morrow.

So you kept your gut and displayed it without shame. It was the same with the women. The wives were bigger in those days big, well built, double-breasted women. Once they were pregnant they never seemed to lose all the weight that they had put on when they were carrying, they were never on a diet, the only weight that they seemed to watch was how to keep it on, and if the woman was small and thin people would say:

'Her's a small oman made of steel, by God her con work. Could do with puttin' on a little weight, though.'

Work, and they did work and you kept out of their way when they were working, like the time when I was watching Uncle Dicky's mother doing a big wash. She was twenty stone and she washed for a living. She was a one-woman laundry and I was in the way so she hit me with a damp cloth right across my legs and it hurt, and I told my mother who said:

'Well, that'll learn ya to keep out of her way.'

The fact was that we had respect in those days and the older you got the more respect you had so that if a baby was about to be born then you fetched Mrs Barr who was an untrained midwife who had had twelve and so knew more about it than the doctor who could not have any because he was only a mon. 'Take away the meat and two veg and there's nothin' left not even a brain'. That's what she used to say about men.

When she came around to birth my sister she told the doctor to make sure that there was some boiling water and to wait downstairs until he was called. She was a big woman who took no lip from the night before. And so the doctor and my Dad smoked Turkish cigarettes and talked about rabbits. Dr Zair bred rabbits, he had created a species that he called the Ashford Giant. He'd done this by crossing a Belgian hare with a Flemish Giant. His rabbits were bred for food. Doctor Zair always drove an open car and hung his stethoscope over the windscreen. If he was in a hurry, he never stopped for Halt signs. We had no traffic lights in our town so that that was never put to the test but on one occasion he drove past the policeman who was directing the traffic on the Bull Ring. It was the policeman's fault, he was a relief from Shrewsbury and did not recognise the doctor's car.

And so there was a crowd gathering in front of the Butter Cross, it was market day, a pig day which meant that the pubs were going to be open all day and it was half term, a quarter past eleven and I was on my way round town and then I had to take the height of the sun.

Across the road walking in front of Hepworths the tailors was an old man with a stick who Joe Wait said would not be long for the box.

'You're uncouth,' my Dad said to Joe.

'Well, you enters the world and then you goes out of the world,' said Joe, 'that's as sure as eggs is eggs. Birth and death, no birth, no death, no death, no birth, first came death, things had ta die so's they was a need fer birth but the only thing that I dunna like doin' is babies, I dunna like that, and I dunna like cremations. I dunna like burnin', it ain't natural, burnin', but I likes burying them when they'se had a good life and I buries em well.'

Just as Joe finished speaking two men and two women came walking down the High Street. The men both wore beards. No one at that time in the history of our town wore beards, it was not the fashion. The only people who wore beards were the 'Bruderhof'. The women of the 'Bruderhof' wore dresses right down to the ground. They were black dresses with leather belts and buckles and they wore home made cardigans and shawls draped over their shoulders. They both carried large shopping baskets. When you saw them in town you thought that was how people dressed during the very olden days.

The 'Bruderhof' were a commune that lived on the side of the Clee Hill. It was a strange and inhospitable place to live. Most people who lived up there worked in the quarry or were smallholders and were poor. The 'Bruderhof' made wooden gates, but they did not shave, even the boys who were almost men did not shave which meant that they had fluff on their chins and so when they came to town our boys used to follow them around, aping the way they walked. So that they became conscious that they were being aped, but they did nothing. They were pacifists which meant that they would do nothing, and because they would do nothing it made them stronger than our boys who became very frustrated.

The other thing was that a half dozen of the girls from the 'Bruderhof' went to the High School, dressed the same way as their mothers, but since they were good intelligent students, then Miss Greyfoot the head mistress let them wear what they wanted to wear. And if Miss Greyfoot let that happen then there had to be a reason because Miss Greyfoot was well in with the Bishop who would have stopped them wearing what they wanted if it was wrong. Discipline was as strong at the High School as the Grammar School. Miss Greyfoot would use the cane, if the cane was necessary. Every girl at the High School knew that if they were caught smoking then they would be caned, all the schools were the same, even if you went to Blackpool you kept looking behind you just in case there was a school boss somewhere about.

My sister had a friend who was in her class at the High School, a 'Bruderhof' girl, she came to our house once and sat on the lawn. Before she sat, she lifted her long skirt and I saw that her legs were long and white and that she wore black knickers. The sight of her legs that were always hidden made me feel strange and I asked her if she was going to the May Fair but she shook her head.

'The Bruderhof,' Cocky said.

'Ha,' said Joe, 'I've never buried one yet.'

'They ain't no uld uns yet,' said Jim .

We all watched the members of the 'Bruderhof' moving up towards the Town Hall.

'Jack,' Jim said, looking at my Dad, 'now what der think of that lot, a commune and all that, like, what does it mean, does it mean that they got nothing to call their own, like you ain't got yer own house or things?'

'A commune means that they all piss in the same pot and shares the kids out at Christmas,' said Joe laughing.

'I think they are displaced persons from Germany and so they had nothin' in the beginning,' my Dad said. 'Perhaps they lost everything they had. It's a German name but they all speaks better English than what we do. All I know is that at this moment they make more gates than any one else around here and that they are good gates and because they are good gates then they can't make enough.'

'There's a farmer over the other side of the hill,'

said Manny, 'he's got five of them gates, started uth one, and he said to me that they was made so well that they'll last a lifetime, so he bought four more. Cheapest gates in the long run, so he told me.'

'An' if a farmer says that, then there must be summat in it,' said Jim Stokes. 'Like the Jews,' he said.

'The Jews?' Cocky said.

'Ah,' said Joe, 'like they just started out in Israel, like, and so they got nothin' 'cept the clothes they stand up in and so they all go into a Kibbutz, that's a commune, in it, Jack?'

'Ah, you're right there, Joe,' Dad said.

'So they all piss in the same pot,' said Joe.

And then the two couples who were from the 'Bruderhof' walked towards us but stopped to look in Fishy Pearce's wet fish shop. The two women went in and left the men standing outside. About five minutes later the women came out. As they passed in front of us my Dad said 'Good Mornin' and Joe Wait said, 'You got some fresh fish, then' and then they all stopped and the woman lifted the linen cover of her basket and we could see about a dozen mackerel in the basket.and there were handfuls of ice on the fish.

'Der yer fry um or bake um?' Joe Wait said.

'Bake them, with herbs,' the woman said and she covered the basket and the four of them smiled at us and then they walked away, and as they walked we saw the women's long skirts almost sweeping the ground.

'Just like the Mademoiselle,' Jim said.

The Mademoiselle was the French lady who ran a small private school in Galdeford for four-year-olds. You could sometimes see them walking about town hand in hand, Mademoiselle urging 'Depechez-vous', or 'Allez allez' as she held out her arms protecting them as they crossed the road, the children singing 'Frere Jacques' as they walked.

It was as if there was a small part of France walking about our town. I so much wanted to go to her school, especially after my father had found out that we had almost Napoleonic ancestry. But there were two things that prevented that. One was that you had to pay and my mother was a Socialist and she believed that all education should be free and that all fee-paying schools should be eradicated. And the other was that Mademoiselle was a Roman Catholic and that she had been seen taking Protestant children into the Catholic church. That was the big sin. My mother was afraid of her mother, whose hatred of Catholics was legendary. Uncle Cliff had married a Catholic. He was the uncle that I had never seen, just his Christmas cards and a postal order, and then he came to visit the family on the bus with Uncle Howard and Aunty Betty, and we all went up to meet them. I will never forget my grandmother shouting as we approached the house:

'NOT OVER THE THRESHOLD'.

She would not let a Catholic enter the house. And then there was a God Almighty row. That subsided when Granny shut herself in the bedroom. And then I saw Aunty Winn for the first time, she looked normal for a Catholic but was frightened as a mouse when she entered the house. She was trembling and she could not kiss us and all the time Grandmother walking about upstairs with her footsteps of hate. So that poor Winn started to cry and uncle Cliff was all the time saying; 'I'm so sorry … Oh … Oh, I'm so sorry.'

It was as if he was apologising for marrying the woman he loved. So they left to catch the next bus back to Birmingham, a two-and-a-half hour forty-mile journey, every village, every bus stop, them with their thoughts and us in that house drinking tea.

'I'll make a pot of tea …

I'll make a pot of tea.'

As if tea would heal the wound.

And still she would not come down.

'Wash the floor!' she shouted down the stairs and then I was in the back room with my Dad and someone said, 'It'll bring on one of her turns' and my Dad whispered, 'It wants summat ta strike her down jead.'

That was the real reason why I could not go to Mademoiselle and learn 'Frere Jacques'.

'Ah … Just like the Mademoiselle,' Jim said, 'her cooks em uth the heads on em …'

'Ah, they does that,' said Manny. 'I knowed a bloke, in the war, it was the First, and they used ta make fish soup, left the heads on em, good soup, it was.'

'I likes the heads off mine,' said Joe. 'Do they leave the heads on em in America, Cocky?' and Joe looked at him as he asked the question and Cocky pinched his nose and then ran his finger under his nose and then he looked at Joe and said:

'There just ain't any fish on the range. Steak is what they eats, steak and beans and black coffee and you've never seen steak like they have in America, like Dinosaur's steaks they be and they even puts a couple of fried eggs on em.'

'I seen him eating Stilton cheese,' said my Dad, pointing to Cocky, 'when it was so ripe that there was maggots coming out and Cocky was eatin' em like a donkey eatin' strawberries and that was at the Gas Board dinner.'

'And you was putting butter on yer knife so that the peas wouldna fall off,' and Cocky was pointing at my Dad, 'and who was it made the farting machine so that you let one rip and then another and then because you'd put too much pressure on the elastic band you ripped the cover of the chair and when old Maddox went to the toilet you changed chairs ...'

And they all started to laugh even the three men waiting for the pubs to open so that there was laughter floating about like confetti until half a dozen girls came round the corner. Girls from the sixth form who had been playing tennis and who would soon go to College. They were not only pretty but in their white short pleated skirts they were astonishingly beautiful, so we all moved out of their way to let them pass as if we were afraid of them.

And so they passed.

Then they were about ten yards away but still we didn't say anything we just followed them, their voluptuous swaying, the haunches balancing and we liked it so much that our eyes followed them all up the High Street.

Until Jim said, 'They ought to be in service, by God, big wenches should be in Gentlemen's service, that ud learn em to cook and clean, then they might make a mon a good wife'.

And it seemed that as they moved the street became flooded by a white sparkling light and as they disappeared out of sight the spell that held us broke.

'Unlike you bastards we got work to do,' Cocky said.

And Cocky and my Dad went off down Broad Street and I went to take the height of the sun.

# 18    *Horace*

I was heavily weighed down with the responsibility of taking the height of the sun. I had to do it at twelve noon every day. Even if the sun did not shine I had to be there just in case it did shine and we were having a lot of overcast days so that I had not taken a reading for three days, which meant that I would have to take a reading today but I did not want to take a reading because my Dad, Uncle Dicky and Kelly were going to Tenbury to paint the gas holder.

'You said that you would do it,' my mother said, 'and if you say that you are going to do a thing then you must do it, you must see it out until the end. You have given your word.'

And so I had to do it, and I was learning that if you do the same thing every day of your life then your life becomes boring and I was twelve years old, my days were moving slowly, I was trapped by a theodolite, the small amount of glamour that I had achieved because I was the one who took the height of the sun was lost when the other boys ran away over the hills like wild ponies. It tempered me when I asked my pocket watch why.

'It will help you to grow up,' my mother said.

Yes, it tempered me, but it did not stop me from getting my bike ready, it did not stop me from going to Tenbury in the afternoon. I could come back with them in the evening.

My bicycle was the most important thing that I owned. It was a Rudge Whitworth, it had a free wheel. I wanted a three speed but the three speed was extra, about six pounds extra. My bike was black and had red and yellow lines, coach built lines that set off the black frame. These lines gave my bike class. They looked like the lines around the boiler of a Fowler 4P tank engine, the kind that used to run from Swansea to Shrewsbury up the central Wales line. I called my bike 'The Black Gnat' and had carefully used a stencil so that the name ran each side of the top crossbar. Mr Gould who owned the post office gave me a postman's hat so that when I fixed a long thin bamboo pole to the rear mudguard my bike had an aerial and I could be a Police patrol man. I had a speedometer from an old motorbike that I'd found on the tip that was accurate when stationary and a large saddlebag attached to the Brooks leather saddle. It was useful for sandwiches, a bottle of cold tea and also for carrying conkers or acorns.

There was a very serious road racer who lived near us. He was six feet six and used to do time trials using a fixed wheel. He suffered from hay fever but was unbeatable except at harvest time when he used to ride with his eyes and nose streaming. He never gave up because he would not permit himself the luxury of coming second. You always knew when he was in a time trial, there was a distant wheezing, strained muscles tensely pumping and then he would shoot by, almost a blur on his twenty-nine inch red frame Claude Butler hand made bike. If you were at the finish he would blow his nose like a foghorn. That blowing would last for ten minutes or more until his face was as red as a beetroot and then he would start shaking his head up and down, his colour very slowly returning to normal, those just red bloodshot eyes full of tears and him nodding his head.

'There are three rules to training,' he used to say. 'Always carry a puncture outfit, take as many left turns as possible and never apply yer front brake.'

I thought about the time trialist and his fixed wheel as I was waiting for the sun to come out.

It was half past eleven when the old grey tom cat slowly walked across the top of the brick wall, his four feet treading tenderly, his white whiskers like fishing lines as the bright blue sky exploded before my eyes and the sun came out and it was perfect, so I took the reading just in case it wasn't there at noon. I was delighted with that cat as I folded the instruments and locked them in the storeroom. Fifteen minutes later I was standing on the pedals of The Black Gnat trying to get him to go up Tinkers Hill and wishing that I had a bike with a three-speed gear.

Once over the top of the hill there was the descent to the crossroad called The Serpent. Always such a draught, such wind, that I had to lean forward, that I had to tie my postman's hat onto the rear saddlebag so that I would not lose it to that gusting. How I looked forward to this air combat, to my green flag fluttering on its little steel flagpole on the tip of my front mudguard. It was beautiful to let yourself be caressed on the lips of that breeze, and all the smells, the wild garlic, the smouldering fire in the garden of the house at the bottom of the hill and the goats that were chained up on the side of the road and the dark damp passage through the overhanging trees so that your body became full of aromas from a windy bath.

The sound of the freewheel ticking until slowing and my legs pedalling and the clean polished wheels glittering in the sun until I stopped and looked at the signpost that said 'Ludlow two miles, Tenbury six miles, Caynham three miles'. I would be there in half an hour. I had never ever been so far from home by myself before, I felt as if I was on a tightrope and that I must continue along it, I could not go back, I was committed, so that it was as if another dimension was opening up before me. I felt that I was about to enter into a world that would be an entirely new sensation and experience. I was on my own. I was touching naked dreams.

At the crossroads to Little Hereford there was the only monkey puzzle tree in our part of the world. I stopped to gaze at it and understood how it got its name. Just up the road was a wide verge and a red telephone box. I had two pennies and decided to call my mother. It was the first time that I had ever used a phone in a call box and I did not know quite what to do so I stood in the call box getting warmed by the sun and listened to the buzzing of the phone and then I replaced it and left it alone and took my bottle of cold tea out of the saddlebag and drank a long deep draught.

The air felt as if it was dull and heavy, only just breathing but those slow breaths had moved the white cotton wool clouds from the summit of Clee Hill so that all the land just below was kneaded together into a green brightness and then a warm and extremely supple wind began to rise and fanned the foliage of the trees so that the branches started to sway and rustle and I looked up and saw that there were a pair of magpies looking down at me so I said, 'Good afternoon, Mr Magpie' and then they both flew out of the tree and into the road about fifty yards ahead of me where they proceeded to peck at the carcass of a rabbit.

I thought about a magpie that I had found fallen out of a nest when I was five. I bottle fed that bird, I took it to school, it became tame, it started to talk, one day it caught a frog and the frog screamed like a baby. The cries were as loud as a baby, it was the most terrible thing that I had ever heard. Jack was just throwing the frog up into the air and all the time the screaming and his evil eyes looking at me when I finally caught him still holding the frog by the neck his beak closing on the frog's throat so that the more I squeezed the bird the more he closed his pincer like beak across the frog's neck and if I released my grip he released his. The bird all the time playing with me until fed up he let go, stepped on the frog, punctured the frog's belly and I saw all the frog's entrails burst out as it screamed a final death scream. I wished that I had never bottle fed that magpie and so before I mounted my bike I lobbed a stone at the two birds on the road.

'You be careful when you comes to that bridge over the branch line just before the main road,' my Dad said when he found out that I was going to bike to Tenbury. 'It's very steep as it comes down to that main road, there's a Halt sign and if you're goin' too fast you won't stop.'

Well, I got to that bridge and then I waited because I'd heard a whistle and I wanted to be on the bridge when the train went under so that I could smell all those pungent gases and taste the unique taste of steam. Railway bridges always reminded me of the time when I coupled my steam engine up to mother's sewing machine so that she would not have to pedal, and it worked but the steam filled the room and she could not see to sew, just the taste of steam.

I sat on the side of the bridge and sliced one of our Irish Peach apples into four and then I removed those parts of the cores that were left and I ate the apple together with one of the cheese sandwiches. It was so good that I did it again and then there was only one sandwich left and no cold tea and I did not know what time it was, so I decided to forget about the steam from the train but by the time that I had got to the junction with the main road the train came. It was a goods train and I waved at the guard who was standing in the guard's van. I waved just in case it was Mr Timmis, who would be angry if he knew it was me cycling along the main road towards Tenbury, too ignorant and arrogant to wave.

Uncle Dicky, Kelly and my Dad would have been painting the gas holder all morning. It would have been very thirsty work, they would have worked fast in order to make time so that they could have a drink. They used the Swan at lunchtime because it was nearest. They would have worked so hard that morning that the time they had saved would have been considerable.

I was surprised they were not in the Swan. I was very surprised when I found them in the bait room in the middle of their dinner time and Uncle Dicky lying on his back right across the bench that normally sat three and my Dad standing in the doorway throwing stones into the pool of black water next to where the tar barrels stood.

'We have been barred from a pub,' my Dad said, 'barred from a fucking pub.'

'We are barred from the Swan.' Uncle Dicky

shouted the words at the tin corrugated roof. 'Barred, barred from a pub, barred, from a pub.'

It was as if the whole world had caved in, there was not an ounce of merriment, instead there was doom.

'Barred,' my Dad shouted each time he aimed a stone at the black water. He never even noticed that I had cycled nine miles in order to be with him.

'Where the hell is Kelly?' Uncle Dicky shouted at the roof. 'That was the biggest mistake that you ever made, that was one great mistake. That will go down in history as your biggest mistake, Jack.'

'No alternative, no alternative,' and my Dad threw another stone at the black water.

'And you gave him ten shillings, you gave him ten shillings. Oh, ten shillings you gave him,' and Uncle Dicky was almost singing until he saw me and then he looked at me standing and he said:

'Your father gave Kelly ten shillings to fetch four quarts of cider from the Rose and Crown. He gave him ten shillings, a note, and him with a throat as dry as a bone he gave him ten shillings over half an hour ago and it does not take a half an hour to go to the Rose and back. Mike, take yer bike and go and see if you can find that little bastard, he's got the works carrier bike' and Dicky lifted himself up from the bench and leaned across the table and said,'We got barred from the Swan' and then he banged his fist onto the surface of that bait room table and the spoons and empty cups jumped into the air.

It was a statement of fact that was so terrible, it was unbelievable that such professional drinkers could be barred from a pub. It was an insult and then my Dad said:

'We should have changed, we should have changed.'

'He could ave let us drink out the back, in the passageway,' said Dicky.

'But he wouldn't, it was the smell of the paint,' Dad said.

And I knew then that my Dad and Dicky were suffering from a great depression caused by being refused a drink and I tried to picture it all in my mind, them going with such a great thirst into the hotel bar and being refused and all the time Dicky would be getting so angry that it would not take much of an excuse to shout at the manager and to perhaps even threaten him in a violent manner, or in the very least to give him a pedigree that would be lower than a snake's belly.

And then I knew that I would have to find Kelly so that they might have a drink and so I nodded to myself that I would find Kelly and I rode off out of the gasworks towards the Rose and Crown with a great desire to help my father and Uncle Dicky and I pedalled with such gusto that I was soon passing the Swan where they had been barred and my heart was beating so fast that those that were in the great bar of that hotel as they saw me moving past, they all looked up and saw a boy on a black Rudge Whitworth bike with a bamboo aerial tied on his back mudguard looking like a policeman on patrol. I saw them watching me but I pedalled on until I saw the Rose and Crown and the gasworks carrier bike leaning up against the front porch and I knew that I'd found Kelly.

Now Charlie Robinson's cider was renowned for its flavour and Kelly was savouring that flavour ever so slowly in the back room bar. He was swallowing down that liquid so tenderly just like my father did when he had already swallowed a pint all at once, so I knew that Kelly had quenched his thirst and was treating the drink like a great lady who was queen of the ball and then someone shouted up from the cellar:

'Six quarts, you wanted six quarts'.

And there were others in the room who were crowding the bar and shouting down at whoever it was below to get a move on because there was only a certain amount of time left in the day and then a man came up with a wooden crate which contained six quarts all wet with cider because they had all overflowed when he had filled them with the small bore rubber pipe that he would have used, just like my Dad used when he filled his quart bottles to store in the great gas fridge. And then the barman lifted the flap of the bar and placed the crate with the six quarts in it on the floor and then I saw him give Kelly his change but before he could put it in his trouser pocket Kelly saw me standing there. And the barman saw me and he said that I should not be standing there that I should wait in the passageway if I wanted something and then Kelly said:

'He's Jack's boy,' and he looked at me.

And I said, 'Mr Baker, Dad sent me to find you.'

And Kelly laughed and said, 'I had ta try it before he filled em, and then I had one while I was waiting,' which seemed to Kelly the most logical thing to do with any spare time that you might have in a pub.

We both hurried our bicycles towards the gasworks, the Black Gnat in front, me turning, riding with one hand because of the pleasurable wind that was trying to lift my peaked cap right off my head.

So there I was, pedalling with all my might, steering with one hand, the other holding my hat as we passed the Swan, all those eyes peering behind the glass window, and Kelly behind holding his two fingers in a V so that those behind the window could see that Kelly was saying 'Right up your kite'. It was like being at war and all the time our legs moving like pistons on a train.

'Where the hell have you been, Kelly?' shouted my Dad and Dicky together.

The sound of their voices was like a wire brush rubbing against sandpaper.

'There were that many in the bar,' replied Kelly, 'it being the dinner hour and Charlie Robinson not there but only the barman, himself rushed off his feet so that I had to wait, him being unable to leave the bar for the ten minutes that it would take to fill the bottles.'

'And I suppose that you had one while you waited,' my Dad said as he walked over towards Kelly who had both feet on the ground holding the bike upright.

'Just to try one, Jack,' replied Kelly respectfully. 'I would not want to bring back tack that was off in any way.'

'I bet you tried more than one,' said Dicky as he helped my Dad remove the wooden crate from the carrier.

'One for me thirst and one for the taste,' said Kelly. ''Tis difficult to judge the taste when you have a great thirst.'

'You old bastard,' said Dad.

'Ya bugger,' said Dicky.

My father and Dicky always seemed to have the proper tackle to drink with. They had two cider horns that were bigger than the ones Dad had in his shed and there was also a selection of half pint glasses in a wooden box that was just behind the door of the bait hut.

When they poured the first of that cider, the

pouring seemed to snatch away the doom and murk that was over the gasworks when I'd first arrived. It was wonderful when Dicky fixed my little flag on its bamboo pole to the ladder and I watched the flag flap on the end of that wooden bamboo every time someone went down that ladder and I watched it move every time someone came up that ladder. And my Dad saw me watching and he said,

'A touch of genius, don't you think?' and I nodded, and Dad said, 'That's why I likes working with Dicky.'

After they had painted another quarter of the roof Dicky sent Kelly down for another quart and then he waved his paintbrush over his head and he said to my Dad:

'Do you know, Jack, I have just had the most brilliant idea ever.'

'What's that?' Dad said still painting..

'The pig, Horace,' Dicky said.

'What about Horace?' Dad said.

'It all came to me when you were chucking stones into them tar pools,' Dicky said. 'I knew then that somehow them pools would be of use. It's only just dawned on me but he loves that pig and Horace would so much love to roll in the mud, that poor pig trapped in that sterile clean backyard sty.'

'No,' my Dad said.

And then I saw them both smoking in silence and I saw Dicky laughing and my Dad grimaced and spat over the edge of the gas holder and they both looked at my aerial on the end of the ladder moving about and they saw that it was Kelly with more cider and when they had drunk that bottle, when they had held each glass in the air and toasted what a glorious day it was and what a wonderful idea Dicky had had, when they had poured the very last drops of cider down their necks, when they had let me drink another half a glass, when my Dad had shouted from the top of the gas holder 'Doh re mi fa so la ti doh! … what makes me fart I do not know', when they had done all that and not much painting, Dicky said:

'Come with me.'

And all three of us went down from the top of the gas holder and we were walking across the yard when Dad said to Dicky:

'How will we make him come?'.

And Dicky said, 'Make a sound like a bucket of pig swill.'

And then he went into the little office by the weighbridge and came out with a bucket. And then the three of us crossed the road towards the Swan Hotel.

I wasn't sure what they were going to do with the pig called Horace once they'd got him out of his pigsty. I assumed that what they were going to do was to capture him, probably lock him up somewhere in the gasworks and thereby make the manager of the Swan worry that he'd lost his pet pig to the butcher.

The pigsty was behind the outbuildings that were at the far end of the car park. It was almost three o'clock and Horace was lying down in that corner of the sty where there was the most sun. Horace was a fat little pig, he was spoilt, he was tame and there was food in his trough so that he was not hungry.

'Get into the sty, Mike,' said Dicky.

And so I climbed over and stood looking at the sleeping pig who was not sleeping but was looking at me standing looking at him. Dad and Dicky were kneeling down looking over the wall.

'He likes being stroked', said Dicky, 'rub him

behind the ears and make friends with him, rub his back, let him get to know you and then open the gate and bring him out round the back of them old sheds so that you can't be seen and then lead him over towards them big horse chestnut trees over there ... that's it ... he'll soon get to know yer ... now open the gate'.

There was a latch on the outside of the gate but I saw the chef's long white hat bobbing about behind the clothes line and so I ducked .

'Open the gate,' said Dicky again.

'I can't, the chef's coming,' I said, turning towards Dad and Dicky who were still looking over the wall. And the pig was still lying down looking at me and then he belched, he belched just like a human and Dicky said:

'He's drunk.'

'He gets all the beer slops,' said Dad, 'that pig lives better than you or me'.

I knelt down beside the pig and scratched him behind the ear and the pig just moved his tail a little and when I stopped scratching he lifted his head and looked at me as if to say carry on. But I didn't and the pig got up and rubbed himself up against me. The pig thought that he was a cat! And then I saw the door open. Uncle Dicky had crawled round and opened the door so that I just walked out with the pig following me.

But the pig would stop and then when I scratched behind his ear the animal would go weak at the knees so that I would have to stop scratching and move a few more steps until I was almost in the cen-tre of the car park. It was nerve racking. I felt that the population of Tenbury could see me enticing the pig. I was on my own because every time the pig saw my Dad and Dicky he would go in the other direction. It was as if he could sense something about them. But he seemed to like me and ran after me when I ran across the car park to the other side where there were two horse chestnut trees.

I hid behind the trees and saw the pig running towards me. He wanted to be scratched. He rubbed up against my legs and knocked me over. As I scrambled to my feet I saw Uncle Dicky coming towards me, he was grinning and the pig was grunting and we were further away from the gasworks than we should have been, but Dicky signalled that I should try to catch some apples that he had found. Horace liked apples and these were large green Bramleys.

I never knew that pigs made so much saliva when they ate until I saw Horace eat the apple. It bubbled from around his teeth and then when he'd finished he ran after me and Uncle Dicky was signalling that I should take Horace right across the field at the edge of town and enter into the gasworks by way of a small wicket gate. It could not have been better, the pig was following me and I was already at the gate and left an apple for him.

And then Horace saw the stream that ran through the gasworks. He made for that stream. There was a strange look of freedom in that pig's eyes as he trotted towards all that black mud.

Horace's sty was dry and clean, he was a pig that was accustomed to being invited into the very lounge of the Swan Hotel. He was an aristocratic pig who had never seen mud, glorious mud. And so Horace wallowed in that mud, he walked knee deep in it and then he rolled in it and where the stream ran through the tar beds Horace rolled so that he became a black pig and I saw that Dad, Kelly and Uncle Dicky were on the top of the gas holder and that they were drinking and that they were laughing and when I climbed the ladder they were on their knees painting away because the landlord of the Swan was out in the street and he was calling:

'HORRACE … HORRRRRRRRACE!'

And the pig rose from the black mud tar and ran out of the gasworks and across the road towards the Swan and the landlord was shouting. The chef came running out of the front double door that had glass engraved panels and led out into the street from a Wilton-carpeted corridor. And the head waiter came running out of the swing doors dressed in his white starched shirt and his black bow tie and then the other waiter in his cutaway coat, and even the old cocker spaniel who peed just as soon as his front paws touched the street.

And the pig galloped towards all of them standing there waving their arms, that poor pig who must have been a little confused because they were all trying to stop him from going into the hotel. An hotel where he'd been treated like a king from birth, where he'd been encouraged to sleep in front of the great wood fire, to lie there like a cat, and so he charged at those double swinging doors and because everyone in the street was dressed as they were, they were all afraid to grab the pig who would walk through the dining room, because he always walked through the dining room, a room more like a room in a manor house with chintz curtains and pots of asparagus ferns and all kinds of freshly cut flowers, whatever happened to be in season, and the landlord of the Swan was screaming and crying and all the time my father and uncle Dicky were painting as fast as they could without lifting their heads and Kelly was opening another can of green paint and stirring it with a long wooden stick and then Kelly straightened himself up and started to roll a cigarette and as he lit it with his petrol lighter he said out of the corner of his mouth:

'The whole shower of them has gone inside!'

And I looked at my father and Uncle Dicky and could see that they were still painting and weeping with mirth.

Weeping with mirth.

# 19   *Cannon*

It was that time in the history of our street when families started to obtain motor cars. Other than the cars that belonged to the very rich, doctors and the Right Rev Carver, the only car permanently seen down our street was Long Un Potts' old Ford that had been nicknamed 'The Silver Bullet' on account of the fact that Long Un had painted it inside and out in aluminium paint. But his car did not count since it was a working car and was used for rabbiting.

Long Un had ripped out all the upholstery, then all the seats, except the driver's. He'd installed rows and rows of hooks so that dead rabbits could be hung inside the car. The 'Silver Bullet' when it moved towards the rabbit warrens had nets on its roof, ferrets and lurchers inside, and Long Un sitting in the driver's seat wearing a red and white spotted neckerchief. I never ever saw him without a neckerchief around his neck, and I can't remember that he ever worked for a master. I doubt that he had time to. He kept pigs, and grew all his own vegetables, he lived off the fat of the land. Whenever anybody saw the car they would say, 'There goes Long Un in the "Silver Bullet".'

So the 'Silver Bullet' did not count as a car. Jack Price's 'Ermintrude' did. It was one of the first cars to be owned by a working man. 'Ermintrude' was an Austin Seven that went every time Jack Price turned the handle. I remember one time in the middle of winter when I used to work part time for Fred Adshead, the log merchant. I used to sit on the back of Fred's truck and fill the baskets with logs. What happened was that as soon as Fred or Mr Wilson took a full basket to a customer then I filled an empty one. It was hard work, and it used to make me sweat. Anyway, Fred had an old Ford petrol truck. It was Saturday morning in the middle of winter, the temperature right at the bottom on both scales. The truck would not have any of it. Fred had made a fire inside an old oil drum, he'd heated every plug, he'd run the battery down, he'd turned the starting handle, and no one who has not turned the starting handle of an eight ton petrol truck, has any idea what it means to turn a starting handle. Old Fred had smoked half a packet of Players, he'd prayed, he'd even thought about fetching Rev Carver to come round and bless the thing because he had to get that truck out on the round because that was how he made a living and we were two hours late and then Jack Price came up to fetch 'Ermintrude' which was garaged right out in the open and was covered in two feet of snow and her windows were frosted up like lavatory windows:

'No way,' said Fred, 'will Pricey start that heap.'

And so we all looked at Jack Price who brushed the snow off the bonnet and lifted it so that we saw that there was just as much snow inside as out, it had entered through the air vents and all the other gaps that there were, because 'Ermintrude' was older than the second world war, and we knew that it was just as cold inside the engine compartment as it was outside and so we all watched Jack Price talk

to 'Ermintrude' and we saw him touch her carburettor and then he took the handle from under
the seat and inserted it into 'Ermintrude' and on
the second turn she started to wobble and then Jack
said to her, 'Bit cowed fer yer, my uld dear,' and
then he turned the handle again and 'Ermintrude'
fired herself up on all fours and then Jack Price
went over to the tap that had been defrosted, filled
the water can and poured water into 'Ermintrude's'
radiator. He then turned to Fred who was dancing
on his flat cap that he'd thrown in a rage on the
floor and said:

'You wants ta drain the engine every evening,
Fred. Ermintrude dana like that glycerine slurping
around inside her. Matter of fact, all engines is
better off without it.'

And then that summer Uncle Dicky bought a
Morris and all of a sudden it seemed that everyone
had a car except us, not that we could not afford
one, it was just that my Dad could not see the reason to have one. For him, everywhere that he
wanted to go he could go on a push bike. He was
the original anti car man. When he was on the
Council it was proposed that the bridge should be
widened so that two cars could pass each other:

'No way,' he protested, 'narrow it, make it harder
to get into town, the car will crucify this town.'

My mother said that he was against all progress,
she used to wring her hands and say that so-and-so
was going to Borth but my Dad used to say that
Borth was like Craven Arms by the sea, 'Take away
the sea and there ain't nothing left,' he used to say.

His idea of a week's holiday was to fill the saddlebag on his bike with a loaf of fresh bread and a
pound of cheese and visit country pubs. 'I can't
think of any better way to spend a week,' he used to

say. 'Look at it this way. You have two weeks' holiday a year, that's one hundred weeks, or less than two years during a working lifetime, that's the only free time you got, the rest of yer life is spent working, two years is hardly any time to see all the land within a distance of ten miles, is it?'

And my mother would cry on her own when she was sewing because she hated pubs and she wanted to go to the seaside. She so much loved the sea, she used to tell us how the sea was made of the same stuff that ran through our veins and that if you lay by the sea you would become all peaceful and relaxed and she so much wanted to send her brothers a card like they sent to us each year saying that the weather was fine, wish you were here. But my Dad had no feelings for the sea. He would sit outside his shed drinking cider, dreaming about imaginary solutions as he smoked his home grown tobacco.

I doubt that he considered his life monotonous, it was just that he was afraid of a spark plug conking out on him, or that he might be driving along somewhere and that the car might suffer from a burnt out piston or that the starter motor might not be able to start the car and that he just did not want that kind of problem miles from anywhere or worse than that, he had a fear that he might crash. He once had a long conversation with our solicitor, Jock Slater, who explained to him the legal problems of driving behind the wheel. He said that the average person had no idea of the responsibility involved, of how many laws that there were, that overall, driving was a full time job best left to a chauffeur.

After that conversation with Mr Slater Dad said, 'I'd get a car', he said, 'if I won the pools, and I'd get a chauffeur as well and then we could visit some

pubs and then yer mother could go to Borth whenever her liked.'

So Dad spent all his life not far from a push bike.
There were not many things that he could not do
with a push bike.

One half term, it was October, our town was
almost empty because of the hop picking, I saw Dad
riding his carrier bike across Dodmore, he was on
his way to fix a cooker for a newly married couple. I
liked to help him. I knew the inside of his great
leather tool bag as well as he did. I knew what a pair
of Footprint spanners were and I liked it when he
soaked his brass blow lamp in methylated spirits
and lit it and he let me blow through the tube so
that there was a long thin blue flame. I liked doing
that.

I'd been to see Granddad who was doing a relief
job as baker in the Co-op. He always made me a
small loaf and then he would put a knob of butter
inside it and I would eat it there in the hot bakehouse and there is nothing like freshly made bread
soaked in butter, so I was really contented when I
saw Dad riding his bike, and I rode with him, me on
the Black Gnat and Dad on his carrier bike to the
house where he was to install a cooker.

When we got there my Dad said that there was
something funny going on

'Looks like a trap,' he said as he knocked the
door.

'Why's that, Dad?' I asked.

'Because there ain't no cooker outside,' he said.

And he was right, there was no cooker.

'Where's the cooker?' he asked the woman who
answered the door.

'I dunno. I hope it's up at my mother's,' she said.

Dad said, 'I was told to come and fix it here.'

'Well,' the woman said, 'I told them about it last week, I told them that it was up at me mother's, she's bought a new one and she's given us the old one.'

'And so has the new one been fixed?' my Dad asked.

'Yes,' the woman replied, 'they were to fix Mum's, she's bought the new one, we had her old one and so they were to take the new one up to her house and bring hers down here and then fix it for me. They said that they would bring it here in the van.'

'And they never did,' Dad said.

'No, and I got nothing to cook on,' the woman said.

'Nothing, not even to make a cup of tea?' Dad said.

'I got nothing,' she said.

'Nothing fer yer mon when he comes home tonight?' Dad said.

'I dunno what I'm gonna do,' she said.

'Where's yer mother live?' Dad asked.

'In the Sandpits,' she replied.

And then my Dad started to lift his cap and he started to scratch his head and then he pulled his pipe out of his pocket and he filled it and then he fired it up with his old petrol lighter so that for a moment there was a great cloud of smoke and the smell of Virginia tobacco. And all the time Dad was smoking the woman was watching and then Dad said that I was on holiday, and that there must have been a misunderstanding.

'We got everything that we might need in the house,' the woman said.

'Excepting the cooker,' Dad said.

'Excepting that,' the woman said.

'So we'll have to get the cooker,' my Dad said and

the woman started to shake her head. 'We'll have to get the cooker so that you can get summat hot on the plate fer yer mon when he comes home', and the woman started to nod her head. 'That's how it should be. We gotta see to it that that's what happens, 'ave we not?' and the woman was nodding and then she said that she had some pork chops.

'Oh, I likes pork chops,' my Dad said, 'how many have yer got?'

'Two,' the woman said, 'big ones.'

'Der like big ones?' my Dad asked, and then the woman started to blush and my Dad told her not to worry. And that was how we were biking across the Sandpits Road at half past ten in the morning and all the time I was thinking about how on earth Dad was going to get that gas cooker from one end of the northside of our town to the other.

The cooker was standing outside the back door of a house opposite Biggs's shop. It was covered in an old sack.

'It's a Cannon,' Dad said, 'Damn good cookers, they are.'

The Cannon was big, it had an eye level grill, it had four legs and when I tried to move it it was as solid as a rock. And so I looked at my Dad and I asked him how he was going to get the thing to the woman's house.

'On the carrier of the uld bike,' he said. And I started to shake my head because there was no way that he could get that cooker on the carrier of his bike.

'Der wanta bet?' Dad said.

But I didn't want to bet because I knew my Dad very rarely lost a bet and I thought about Tweedle-dum and Tweedle-dee.

'Put a shilling on it,' he said.

'Naaw,' I said.

My Dad opened his tool bag that was still on his carrier and removed a spanner. He started to undo the nuts at the back of the cooker and then he removed the eye level grill and then he removed the back so that the cooker looked strange and was almost half its normal size.

He lifted all the burners and the gas pipes that fed the jets. And then he removed the door and he lay the cooker on its side and removed the four legs, all the time putting all the screws in his pocket.

In no time the cooker was stripped. And then he put all the loose parts into the carrier and he put the back of the cooker onto the carrier and then we cycled back to the woman's house and we laid all the parts on the floor of her kitchen with Dad's tool bag and then we went back and collected the door, all the interior shelves and the legs, so that all that was left was the oven and then we went back for the oven.

That oven was heavy, it was cast iron, it was an old fashioned oven that would hold its heat. It was about the weight of ten modern gas cookers that are made out of old sardine cans, the kind you can buy from an out of town shopping centre, the kind whose fittings fall off the day after the guarantee expires and sometimes even before that, the kind that can hardly generate enough heat to defrost an instant meal from the freezer.

What I'm talking about was an oven, a common oven, the kind of thing Mrs Beeton would have used, the kind that can roast a joint, the kind that raises the pastry on an apple pie, the kind that you can no longer purchase, the kind of oven that can bake a loaf of bread, because the oven holds a constant heat, the kind that a man and a boy cannot lift onto the carrier of a carrier bike.

We tried, we did lift it, but then my Dad said, 'Put it down'. I could not understand why. 'The thing of it is,' my Dad said when we'd got it back on the deck, 'You have to understand something of the relationship between man and bike.'

I thought that my Dad was going crazy, I looked at him, he was cleaning out his pipe, he was scraping burnt ash from the bowl of his pipe:

'I bin waiting to do this fer a long time,' he said.

And then when he'd blown through the stem of his pipe and it sounded as if it was completely clear, he took out his leather pouch and filled his pipe with tobacco that he had cured from his own plants and then he fired up and there was the most wonderful smell of Virginia tobacco hanging in the air and when he'd got the pipe smouldering correctly he said:

'The relationship between man and bike is a special relationship based on the fact that the man is a part of the machine, der you understand?' I nodded. 'One is no good without the other. For example, we are trying to lift this cooker onto a machine that will tip once the said weight is on that machine without the person who is in control of that machine being on the machine, which means that the bike is no good without the person on the machine, which means that the person is therefore part of that machine ... you see, the bike becomes part of the human and the human becomes part of the machine.'

'It won't go without someone on it,' I said. 'It will fall over unless I balance it'.

'Correct,' Dad said, 'unlike a car or a horse, you cannot put a dead man on it, it will fall over, which means that the thing is useless without a living mon on it so the relationship of the one with the other is imperative, unlike a horse which can live and move without a mon.'

'It's the same for a car,' I said.

'A car is a more independent thing,' Dad said. 'Put a dead mon in it at the top of the hill and it will run away, it will for a limited amount of time lead a life of its own, on its own, but a bike can't move without a mon, which means that the bike is almost organic and therefore it is the most friendly of devices that we have ever invented ... it is an enabler.'

I looked at my Dad smoking his pipe and using a word that I'd never heard before.

'An enabler?' I said.

'You won't find it in the dictionary, I've just invented that word, I'll explain ... A human being on his own two feet is capable of moving wherever he wants in whatever direction he wants at a little over four miles an hour ... right? The only improvement on this degree of mobility is a bike which can move at three times that speed with ease and downhill at an even greater speed ... right? Pass that threshold and you have to have an engine, which means that you have to buy the energy to increase speed and to do that you have to have money to buy the fuel and that is why the rich have that power, which means that you have to have an equality difference between the man without money so that only a few can have the pampered travel on a magic carpet which enables them to travel between distant points that they would not be able to travel to in the first place and so the faster they go the longer they travel and then they spend more time travelling to somewhere that they do not need to go to in the first place and the faster they go the less they see, so they might as well not have gone there at all ... do you see?'

I nodded, 'Pataphysics,' I said.

'Pataphysics is a true science,' Dad said, 'it's the science of imaginary solutions. Don't get it mixed up with the science of real problems like the need to be somewhere else which is an imaginary problem because we only imagine that we have to be somewhere else.'

Listen..listen ...

Is that the sound of a motorbike, go out, and if that's ... Bill Massey the signal man on his Norton then wave him down. He can help lift the oven on the bike.

Bill Massey was a scrambler, he had a three-fifty single Norton that he used to race. I spent hours watching him strip down the engine after every race. I knew that it had a compression ratio of 10.8:1, that the carburettor was one and three sixteenths, that the crankcase was a two piece forging in steel and that he used SAE 20 oil that was fed into the gear box at the rate of 30 gallons an hour and that its running temperature was 60 degrees on the centigrade scale. I knew more about Bill Massey and his bike than Dad did, so I rushed out onto the road and I waved him down and his eyes were all bloodshot because he was not wearing goggles and his face was all dried up tears and he stopped his bike and he balanced it on his two feet because he had stripped the centre stand and the side stand so that it was better for racing.

'Hey Bill,' my Dad said, 'we got a problem with an oven. I've tried shouting at it, but it won't jump up onto the carrier of the bike and we got an oman down the road who as just moved house, just married, she is, and her mon is out workin' and she has no cooker to cook his tea when he gets 'ome, like, and a woman who can't get a mon his tea is in a sorry state on account of the fact that he will be working away and thinking about the two pork chops that he thinks will be on the plate but won't be unless I can get this oven on the carrier of my bike.'

And then Bill Massey started to laugh and he lifted his right leg over and he stood there holding the bike and then my Dad realised that he could not stand the bike, that the machine would not stand on its own and so he shouted at me to stand on the pavement and to hold the handlebars of that great bike and to make sure that I held it upright and that if for one moment I did not hold it upright then the beast would fall on me and break my legs.

And that was the first time that I held a motor-bike. And as I held it I watched Bill Massey and Dad carry out the oven to the pavement and Dad brought his bike to the pavement and sat on it and Bill lifted the oven, on his own he lifted that oven right onto the carrier of my Dad's bike and I saw Bill's dirty black oily hands with the twisted fingers that had been broken last year when he ran into a tree and just before it was all over, when Bill Massey stood back from his lifting and Dad was thanking him, I twisted the accelerator on his bike just to see what it was like. It felt good.

I thought about what my Dad had said about machines and I was confused.

Back at the house the woman who was just a bit older than the girl next door was standing in the middle of her kitchen looking at the parts of her cooker which were all over the floor.

She seemed worried and did not know what to

do. She had some apples in a large basket. They were Cox's Orange Pippins. She offered them to us but my Dad declined, saying that the only time he had apples was when he drank the juice in the form of cider. She laughed and took one from the basket and rubbed it against her chest, as she rubbed it across her chest, her bosoms moved. The moving bosoms stopped my father dead in his tracks, he was looking up at her as she put the apple into her mouth, he watched her bite into it, he listened to the audible bite and then we could both smell the fragrance of her breath, a moist sweet fragrance from the apple's foam and then my father saw that the woman had bare feet. He looked at her feet and said:

'You'll catch yer death of cold walking around barefoot on them tiles like that.'

'No' she said, 'I always walk around like that, I've always got hot feet.'

'God,' my father said, letting out his breath and smiling, 'you'll make your mon a good wife.'

Then Dad and I were moving the oven into her kitchen and laying it on its side so that Dad could screw the legs on to it, him all the time looking up at the woman while he fished around in his pocket for the nuts and bolts.

It was quiet in that room, just the sound of her eating and the sound of Dad screwing the legs back on the cooker. And then we lifted the cooker upright and Dad fitted the gas pipes that fed the jets and then he fitted a flexible pipe so that the cooker was connected and all the time he was talk-ing to the woman about apples and how it was that the Cox's Orange Pippin got its name. How in the old days they used to put the seeds from an apple into a pot and then cover it with lemon leaves or orange leaves because they thought then that the new apple would take on the taste of the leaves. And he told her that out of ten pips that grew only one would be an eating apple, he told her about an apple called the 'Leather Coat' and how Bardolph was offered a dish of 'Leather Coats' in *Henry 4th*, Part One.

'So they must have been about in uld Bill Shakespeare's time,' he said. 'And did you know that there was an apple called "Costard" that cost a shilling a pound in 1296 and that the average wage was only twenty-one shillings a year and that it was one of the oldest apples in the world and that only its name remained being preserved in the name "Costermonger" meaning the purveyor of "Costard" apples'.

All the time he worked, my Dad talked, occasionally looking up at her, watching her throw away the stem of her apple and her watching her cooker reassembled in her kitchen, standing there with her arms folded.

It was the first time that I understood why women folded their arms.I never realised why Mrs Parsons always ran down the road with her arms folded, I never understood that until I was sitting on the floor of that kitchen with my father and looking up at the woman, her arms folded holding her breasts on her folded arms and apple foam shining on her teeth. I felt that I would like her to kiss me and I did not know why, so it was a great relief when my Dad turned on the gas and said to her:

'Now you can make a cup of tea.'

And then she was apologising for the fact that she only had a box of broken biscuits and my Dad was saying why buy them whole when you can get them a quarter of the price broken and assorted to boot and anyway they get broken up by yer teeth.

'I never thought that you would do it,' the woman said.

'What?' Dad said.

'The cooker,' she said.

'You'd be surprised what I can do if I've a mind to,' and my Dad handed her his empty cup and saucer.

'Just the oven door,' he said, and then I held the door so that Dad could push the first screw through the hole.

'And let me tell you, my dear,' Dad said, 'I'll bet that you got a much better oven than the one yer mother's got … her oven might be newer but you got a real solid cast iron oven there, you'll be able to bake a bun in that oven in no time, that oven will really roast a joint.'

When Dad had finished fitting the oven door he had one nut left in his pocket:

'One nut,' he said, 'one nut left, just like when I took the engine on the motor bike apart, had one nut left. Strange,' he said as he grabbed hold of the cooker and tried to rock it. But it never moved an inch. In fact that Cannon gas cooker looked almost new. And the woman leant forward and polished the name and as she rubbed with her cloth she lifted her right foot and rubbed it up and down against the rear of her left leg so that the rubbing and the movement of her foot looked connected in some strange way. And then I was aware that my Dad was watching me looking at the woman bent over her cooker, polishing:

'Take the tool bag out,' he said.

Outside I felt a decent sun
like soft smoke falling from the sky

and as I lifted Dad's tools
into the carrier of his bike
I sucked my tongue in a little
suddenly I understood
that the sun was not enough